INTROGRESSIVE
HYBRIDIZATION

INTROGRESSIVE
HYBRIDIZATION

Edgar Anderson

(Facsimilie of the 1949 edition)

HAFNER PUBLISHING COMPANY
New York and London
1968

Printed and Published by
HAFNER PUBLISHING COMPANY, INC.
31 East 10th Street
New York, N.Y. 10003

Library of Congress Catalog Card Number: 68-22121

Printed in U.S.A. by
NOBLE OFFSET PRINTERS, INC.
NEW YORK 3, N. Y.

To My Students
With pleasure in what they have learned
With pride in what they have taught me

Foreword

This little book is concerned with hybridization under those circumstances which we so glibly refer to as "natural conditions," that is, with the results of hybridization outside the laboratory and the breeding plot. It passes no judgments on the importance of hybridization in evolution but attempts to take this whole problem outside the area of argument and opinion and into the zone of measurement and analysis. It is very largely concerned with how the effects of hybridization can best be measured in natural populations and with a discussion of the forces at work in such populations.

Most of the techniques presented here are comparatively simple ones that have been developed for analyzing interspecific and intraspecific variation. Observation and measurement are used much as in traditional taxonomic work but refined to a point where they can be employed for analysis as well as for description. By means of such techniques it is now possible for a trained observer to work intensively with a hybrid population in a region completely new to him and from it to deduce exact descriptions of the hybridizing species, even when he has never seen that species (see pp. 43 to 48 and 92 to 99).

Any field of study that is in the process of shifting from the descriptive phase to the analytic phase is certain to suffer from growing pains. This one is no exception. The first methods used were crude, and the ones described below need further improvement.

This book is a step forward in that the relevant literature is now brought together for the first time. Previous presentations have been piecemeal. The basic theory appeared in genetic journals (Anderson, 1939b); applications to taxonomic problems, in taxonomic journals (Anderson and Turrill, 1938; Anderson and Hubricht, 1938); and practical applications to plant breeding problems, in still other places (Anderson and Hornback, 1946). This previous division of the subject matter was not capricious. It resulted from the fact that the concept of introgression was merely a by-product of my long-continued (and still continuing) absorption with the genetics of multiple-factor characters. Therefore, not only has a well-rounded discussion of the work on introgression never previously been attempted, but also a good deal of what is presented below has never appeared in print. On the other hand, the bibliography is limited to cited works, since an inclusive bibliography on introgression by Dr. Charles Heiser is shortly to appear.

This is largely a book about methods for studying hybridization in the field. It is to be hoped that application of these methods and their consequent refinement will produce data from which eventually we can estimate the relative importance of hybridization in evolution.

In this book the more usual methods of analyzing hybridization (transplant studies, cytological analysis, pedigree culture, repetition of suspected hybridization) receive little more than passing mention. It goes without saying that these methods should be used whenever the facilities for them are at hand. All these techniques were employed in the special studies of Tradescantia, Iris, and Nicotiana, from which these newer methods derive their theoretical and experimental verification. It should be emphasized, however, that from a corollary of the demonstration of multiple-factor linkage (see p. 43) we have a new and powerful criterion for hybridity.

Furthermore, the general method (pp. 92 to 99) of extrapolated correlates (and the more specialized techniques here described as "pictorialized scatter diagrams," radiate diagrams, standardized photographs, etc.) have proved to be of wide adaptability in analyzing the effects of such hybridization. Though these methods are here described in full for the first time, they have been rather widely used by my students and colleagues.

EDGAR ANDERSON

Missouri Botanical Garden
St. Louis, Mo.
January, 1949

Contents

CHAPTER 1

Introgression in Iris:
A Typical Example

Before we can discuss introgressive hybridization intelligently we must know what it is like. This first chapter attempts to define the phenomenon and then to give a description of one particular example. Detailed analyses of hybridization under natural conditions have shown that one of its commonest results is repeated backcrossing of the hybrids to one or both parents. With each successive backcross the partially hybrid nature of these mongrels becomes less apparent; the end result of each hybridization is an increased variability in the participating species. The possible importance of this gradual infiltration of the germplasm of one species into that of another was suggested by Ostenfeld in 1927. The process was specifically discussed in 1938 (Anderson and Hubricht) and named "introgressive hybridization." Its consequences were described as the "introgression" of one species *into* another, this terminology being deliberately chosen because it simplified the discussion of particular cases and avoided needless repetition. Introgression has since then been investigated in various genera of the higher plants, and its importance among the vertebrates has been demonstrated, at least for fishes and for Amphibia. Heiser has reviewed the literature on introgression critically (1949) and discussed its probable evolutionary and taxonomic significance.

For the purposes of this monograph one of the best *examples* of introgression is provided by two conspicuous irises of the Mississippi Delta. The scientific data concerning it are widely scattered in genetical, ecological, taxonomic, and horticultural literature, but when they are all assembled they agree, even to details. There can be little doubt that the interpretation presented below is as valid an explanation as one may ordinarily hope to find for complex natural phenomena. It has been studied taxonomically by Foster (1937), cytologically by Randolph (1934), genetically by Riley (1938, 1939a, 1939b), and ecologically by Viosca (1935). The evidence from Reed's experimental genetical analysis (1931) of a closely related cross has been confirmed by numerous horticulturists who have repeated the hybridization of the species from the Delta for garden purposes. Anderson has investigated the problem in both the field and the breeding plot. Riley, Foster, Viosca, and Anderson are in virtual agreement concerning the following account, though they have worked at different institutions and employed differing techniques.

The two species concerned, *Iris fulva* and *Iris hexagona* var. *giganti-caerulea*,* are strikingly different. In appraising the results of any hybridization, the problem is usually simplified if there are such conspicuous, manifold, clear-cut differences between the hybridizing entities as those which distinguish Fulva from HGC. The outstanding differences between these two species are presented in tabular form in Table 1, and a few details are illustrated in Plate 1. For those who have never seen these two irises, it is difficult to overemphasize how strikingly they differ. Though they cross easily and the hybrids have a considerable measure of fertility, they do not seem to be closely related. HGC is certainly more closely allied to *Iris hexagona* of the eastern seaboard and to *Iris brevicaulis* of the northern Mississippi Valley than to Fulva, from which it differs conspicuously in color, color pattern, size, habit, and ecological preferences. Fulva has smallish flowers of the color of old red brick; those of HGC are large with a brilliant pattern of dark blue, light blue, and white, set off by a signal patch of bright yellow. Its relatively few flowers are held crisply erect, whereas

* Since these names are cumbersome and no generally accepted common names are available, they will be shortened to "Fulva" and "HGC" in the following discussion.

TABLE 1

Plant Number	Tube Color	Color of Sepal Blade	Sepal Length (cm.)	Petal Shape	Stamens	Style Appendages	Crest	Index Value	Percentage Pollen Fertility
			HGC						
1	g	Pale violet-blue	9	g	g	g	g	17	95
2	g	Violet-blue	9	g	g	g	g	16	94
3	g	Violet-blue	9	g	g	g	g	17	97
4	g	Blue-violet	9	g	g	g	g	17	95
5	g	Pale blue-violet	10	g	g	g	g	17	94
6	g	Pale blue-violet	9	g	g	g	g	17	96
7	g	Pale violet-blue	11	g	g	g	g	17	92
8	g	Dark violet	9	g	g	g	g	16	92
9	g	Blue-violet	9	g	g	g	g	17	89
10	g	Blue-violet	9	g	g	g	g	17	98
			Fulva						
301	f	Red	5	f	f	f	f	0	98
302	f	Red	6	f	f	f	f	0	97
303	f	Red	6	f	f	f	f	0	99
304	f	Red	6	f	f	f	f	0	95
305	f	Pale red	7	f	f	f	f	1	95
306	f	Red	6	f	f	f	f	0	99
307	f	Pale red	6	f	f	f	f	0	98
308	f	Red	6	f	f	f	f	0	95
309	f	Red	6	f	f	f	f	0	99
310	f	Red	6	f	f	f	f	0	97
			Hybrid Colony H-1						
101	i	Dark red-violet	7	f	i	i	g	8	76
102	g	Pale violet-blue	10	g	g	g	g	17	94
103	i	Red	6	f	i	f	i	3	72
104	g	Pale blue-violet	10	g	g	g	g	17	95
105	i	Red-violet	7	i	g	i	f	8	52
106	i	Very dark violet	8	i	i	g	g	12	96
107	g	Pale violet-blue	10	g	g	g	g	17	94
108	i	Pale violet	9	g	g	i	g	14	85
109	i	Dark red-violet	8	i	i	g	i	10	66
110	i	Dark red-violet	8	g	g	g	i	12	70
			Hybrid Colony H-2						
214	g	Violet-blue	9	g	g	g	g	17	92
215	g	Pale violet-blue	10	g	g	g	g	17	96
216	g	Blue-violet	10	g	g	g	g	17	93
217	g	Violet-blue	10	g	g	g	g	17	98
218	g	Pale violet-blue	9	g	g	g	g	17	98
219	g	Violet-blue	9	g	g	g	g	17	95
220	i	Dark red-violet	7	i	g	g	i	10	80
221	g	Blue-violet	9	i	g	g	g	16	96
222	g	Pale violet-blue	10	g	g	g	g	17	94
223	i	Dark violet	8	g	i	f	i	9	62

those of Fulva droop as if half wilted, one above the other, from successive internodes. Examination of the flowers reveals that Fulva has a red pigment over a yellow ground color; HGC, a blue pigment on a white ground.

When HGC and Fulva are hybridized, the most conspicuous results are due to the recombinations of these two ground colors (and their various intermediates) with the two sap colors (and *their* intermediates). Although such hybrids have never been subjected to detailed genetic analysis, the cross has been repeatedly made for garden purposes by various hybridizers. The *Bulletin of the American Iris Society* from 1930 to 1945 contains frequent reference to these and similar hybrids, occasionally with full descriptions of some of the segregates. Reed, however, has given a fairly detailed report (1931) on experimental hybrids between *Iris brevicaulis* and Fulva. Since *I. brevicaulis* is closely related to HGC (differing from it mainly in its low zigzag stem), Reed's results can be applied directly to the analysis of natural hybridization between Fulva and HGC, the more readily since they agree with those obtained by practical breeders.

As Reed's experimental results indicate (see in particular his colored Plate 1), bizarre recombinations are formed in the second generation and in backcrosses when the pigment genes segregate more or less independently of the ground-color genes. The differences between red pigment vs. blue and white ground color vs. yellow each seem to be multifactorial, so that for the first we get a whole series from blue to purple to red, and for the second a similar transition from white to ivory to light yellow to bright yellow. In the second generation we may get a blue pigment more or less like that of HGC on top of a yellow ground color; the result will be a flower with soft tones of ashy gray. At the other extreme we may get the red of Fulva over the white ground color of HGC, resulting in a delicate rose pink. HGC, furthermore, varies from plant to plant in the strength of its blue pigment, some plants being practically albinos. If this extreme is carried

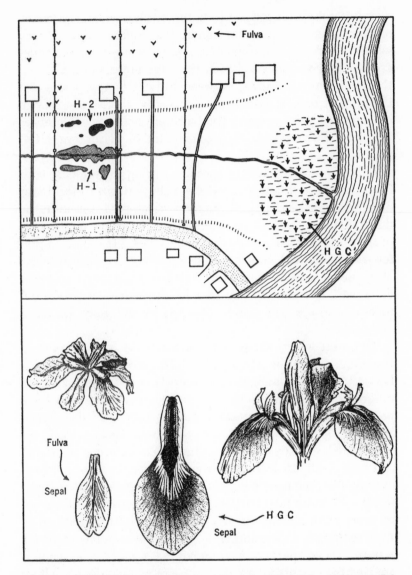

PLATE 1. *Below:* Flowers and enlarged sepals of *Iris fulva* (left) and *Iris hexagona* var. *giganti-caerulea* (right) to the same scales. *Above:* Map of area where these two species were hybridizing. H-1 and H-2 are the hybrid colonies diagrammed in Figs. 22 and 21, respectively.

over into a hybrid, the resulting flower may be largely yellow or ivory, depending on its underlying ground color. Along with these recombinations of the color genes go various degrees of intermediacy between the large flowers of HGC and the small ones of Fulva, between Fulva's floppy petals and the upright ones of HGC. Undoubtedly, there must as well be segregation for some of the basic physiological differences that limit Fulva prevailingly to one kind of a situation, HGC to another.

Fulva is a wide-ranging species growing in wet clay soils from the Wabash and Ohio River valleys down to the lower delta of the Mississippi. Characteristically it is found in the flat valleys of these large rivers along the edges of the natural levees that they build for themselves. It seems to prefer semishade and very often grows along drainage ditches. HGC never gets far from the sea; it is a plant of the lower delta and is found in full sun in the mucky soil of tidal marshes, where the soil is never acid and may be quite alkaline.

The area where these two species come into contact is, therefore, the lower Mississippi Delta, mostly in the region between New Orleans and the sea. It is flat country where differences of a few inches in the height of the land have more effect on the vegetation than hundreds of feet might have in other parts of the world. (Viosca, 1935.) Here, for thousands of years, the river has been building its delta, splitting itself up into numerous weaving branches, which change their courses constantly and sometimes catastrophically. In those rare portions of this rich agricultural region in which man has not greatly altered the natural pattern of the vegetation, Fulva and HGC come into contact whenever a natural levee penetrates a marsh, as, for instance, when a shifting bayou cuts across the course of an abandoned deltaic stream. At such places a few hybrids are sometimes to be found where a natural levee runs into a wide tidal marsh. Hybridization between Fulva and HGC must have been going on occasionally for a very long time. The whole pattern of relationship between these two species, however, has been greatly changed by human occupation. The delta region was settled mainly by the French, and for more than a century little French farms have lined the rivers and bayous. Property lines run straight back at right angles to the rivers. Each family's holding is long and narrow, so that all through the countryside the houses are close together. There has been little large-scale farming. The whole covering of natural vegetation has not been wiped clear as in much of the cotton belt. The average family has cleared some lands for fields, left others in pasture, and has kept a good deal of woodland from which small amounts of cordwood and timber are cut from time to time.

This outline of the two species and the environment in which they meet presents the two fundamentals of the Fulva-HGC interaction on the Mississippi Delta: (1) The two strikingly different but interfertile species, (2) largely kept apart by dissimilar natural environments, progressively altered in part by thousands of small farmers, no two of whom treated their small holdings in exactly the same fashion but few of whom obliterated entirely the natural vegetation. By the early 1900's observant local naturalists were beginning to comment on the results. From New Orleans southward, in many a small community there would be cow pastures brilliant with many-colored irises, white, yellow, wine-colored, red, and blue, many of them so attractive that they were moved into nearby gardens. Eventually, Dr. John K. Small, of the New York Botanical Garden, called them to the attention of botanists and iris gardeners, illustrating them in full color and describing them as species new to science (1927; Small and Alexander, 1931). From the first, both among botanists and iris gardeners, there were those who suggested that the whole complex was of hybrid origin, and eventually Viosca's careful ecological survey of the problem convinced all but a few. Foster came to the same conclusions independently on taxonomic and cytological evidence, and Riley's investigations confirmed and extended

those of Viosca. Meanwhile, the horticultural world took a
deep interest in the beautiful chance hybrids of these remote pastures. Hardier and more generally satisfactory hybrids eventually were bred artificially, but until these man-
made hybrids reached the market in quantity there was
a brisk local business in the brilliant mongrel iris populations of these little agricultural communities of the lower
delta.

Riley's intensive studies (1938, 1939a, 1939b) of these
hybrids were made at one of the localities where Viosca had
discovered a particularly brilliant group. An old abandoned
deltaic stream had built up two levees, one of which served as
a base for the public road. One of the bayous of the river
had swung out, cutting across these ancient ridges and form-
ing a wide marsh in which there were numerous plants of
HGC. Fulva occurred sporadically along the edge of the
abandoned stream for several miles along the road. At the
very point where these two habitats met, there was a series of
small, neighboring farms, their property lines stretching back
at right angles to the road and the abandoned natural levee.
Each family had managed its property a little differently,
and the holdings were all so narrow that the whole community was almost like a laboratory experiment. At several
places there were occasional iris plants that were typical of
neither Fulva nor HGC and might possibly have been of
partially hybrid origin. On one farm, however, there were
great numbers of peculiar irises, most of them resembling
the hybrids obtained by the iris breeders from controlled pol-
linations. They grew in two main groups (H-1 and H-2 in
Plate 1). The H-2 group was rather similar to HGC, and
some of its members were within the variation range of that
species. On the whole they looked like a population of HGC
slightly more variable than usual, but if one tabulated the
variation it was mostly *in the direction of Fulva*. That is to
say, the flower colors tended a little more towards red on the
average; there were more small flowers; there were more
frequently several flowers on a stalk; and the petals were not

all held so stiffly upright as on a typical HGC. The H-1 group was a brilliant mixture. It varied from plants looking more or less like HGC to others resembling the artificial F_1 to a few others more like Fulva. The flowers were large on some plants, small on others. Petal and sepal shape differed from plant to plant. The colors ranged from deep blue to red, with many variations in the size, shape, color, and pubescence of the signal patch. The spot at which this hybrid swarm was growing was the abandoned bed of the old deltaic stream. On this particular farm the land had mostly been cleared, and then a second-growth woodland had been allowed to come up in the depression. This had again been cut over heavily, and the whole area had been overpastured. So many cattle had been kept on the area that the shrubs in the swamp had been browsed. There was much bare soil and relatively little grass, and in the softer ground of the swamp the cattle had created "buffalo wallows" by their attempts to get through in wet weather. On the adjoining farms the overpasturing was not so evident. The woods on one had been almost entirely cleared from the depressions and replaced by a healthy stand of grass. On the other, the second-growth woodlot had been preserved with little cutting over and very little pasturing.

These facts are described in such detail because this particular case is a really critical experiment for understanding the dynamics of hybridization. The bizarre hybrid swarm, H-1, *was entirely limited to this greatly disturbed area.* On one side the hybrid plants went up to the very fence line of the adjoining property but no farther. On the other side they did not quite extend to the fence line. In this little bit of repeatedly cut-over and heavily pastured woodland, adjacent to the spot at which the two species were in contact, there were many more hybrids than in all the rest of the vicinity put together. The reasons for this connection between the disturbance of the habitat and the results of hybridization will be discussed in the next chapter; for the present it needs to be pointed out merely that such a connection is typical of many of the instances of hybridization that have been carefully studied in the field.

Riley made population samples of Fulva, HGC, and various hybrid colonies. Table 1 shows the kind of basic data that he obtained from a colony of HGC, a colony of Fulva, and the two hybrid colonies H-1 and H-2. For each plant he recorded whether it was essentially like HGC, like Fulva, or intermediate in its tube color, petal shape, stamen exsertion, style appendages, and shape of crest. He also measured the sepal lengths, recorded the ground color of the sepal with the aid of a standard color chart, and determined the percentage of fertile pollen in each plant. Table 1 shows the kind of results he obtained for ten plants from each of the four colonies. HGC is essentially uniform in all these characters. Fulva was similarly uniform, varying only in whether the plants were red or pale red. Scored by the same method, the two hybrid colonies presented a very different picture and (a most important point) they showed significant differences between themselves. Both of them varied from plant to plant, but the variation in Colony H-1 was many times as striking. H-1 varied in its extremes for each character and in its combinations of characters. It will be noted that there are no two plants with exactly the same combination of characters.

Colony H-2 was much more uniform. Some of its plants were indistinguishable from HGC; others showed a few slight differences on close scrutiny; a few were clearly intermediate; and, in such measurable characters as sepal length, the population as a whole is slightly more like Fulva than HGC normally is.

Table 1 shows that variation in fertility parallels the morphological variation. Fulva and HGC have pollen of high fertility; there is more sterility in the hybrid colonies, and much more in H-1 than in H-2.

To summarize all these facts in a rough kind of way, Riley used a method originated by Anderson (1936*d*) which is described and discussed in Chapter 6. He arbitrarily as-

signed values to the seven morphological characters recorded in Table 1 and set the scores in such a way that resemblance to HGC was always high in value and resemblance
to Fulva low in value. This procedure produced an index
running from 0 to 17. The calculated index values for the
ten representative plants are shown in Table 1. In his Fig. 3
the combined scores for all the plants of each colony were
shown graphically. The plants of Fulva have uniformly low
values; those of HGC are uniformly high. Colony H-2 is
much like HGC but has a slight trend in the direction of
Fulva. Colony H-1, on the other hand, is in general a mixture of everything from intermediates to plants closely resembling HGC.

The presentation of Table 1 and Plate 1 completes the description of hybridization between Fulva and HGC. In
succeeding chapters we shall discuss the ways in which the
results of interspecific hybridization are controlled by the
dynamics of the environment, by the dynamics of the germplasm, and by the interactions of these forces in actual
populations. We shall continue to refer to this example. It
has been well documented by Viosca and by Riley (in addition to the papers cited above, there are others on pollen
fertility and on developmental rates). It serves the better as
illustrative material because it demonstrates features that
we shall notice again and again when other examples of hybridization are described in detail: (1) the relation between
the effects of hybridization and man's disturbance of the
habitat, (2) the differences between various hybrid populations made between the same species and in the same region,
(3) the predominance of mongrels of partially hybrid ancestry which closely resemble one of the participating species.

CHAPTER 2

The Ecological Basis
of Introgression

From the facts described in the first chapter it is evident that the environment exerts a powerful control over the results of natural hybridization. So powerful is it that we may well begin our discussion of the dynamics of hybridization by considering the effect of the habitat and postpone until the third chapter a discussion of the dynamics of the germplasm itself.

A connection between hybridization and disturbed habitats has long been apparent to observant naturalists. Wiegand in 1935 made it the subject of a special essay (1935). At about this same time Anderson initiated a program (Anderson, 1936*d*) to determine the evolutionary importance of hybridization in Tradescantia. The effect of hybridization was discussed in a series of papers, in one of which (Anderson and Hubricht, 1938, pp. 309, 402) the essentials of the relation between hybridization and the ecological pattern of the habitat were briefly described. This relation was summarized by Dansereau (1941, p. 60) in his study of introgression in Cistus. In several of his papers on speciation in Vaccinium, Camp (see particularly 1942*a*, pp. 200–201) described the way in which the results of hybridization are affected by the dynamics of the habitat, illustrating his argument with examples. Similar situations were described by a number of other investigators, and in 1948 Anderson presented a generalized theory (1948) that will be the main subject of this chapter.

The essentials of the argument are as follows: Hybrids segregate in the second and successive hybrid generations; the habitat ordinarily does not. The flood of hybrid segregants which could result from a species cross is screened out by the nonsegregating habitat in which they would have to live. As a consequence, it is only where man or catastrophic natural forces have "hybridized the habitat" that any appreciable number of segregates survives. It will be well to expand this condensation and outline the critical evidence on which it is based.

The key to understanding the reaction between hybrid segregates and the environment is the realization that habitat preferences are inherited in substantially the same fashion as any other character. We now know that physiological differences are inherited in the same way as morphological ones; some of them are single-factor differences, whereas many of them are multifactorial. The lower organisms are more practical subjects for laboratory research, and it is in such fungi as Neurospora (Beadle, 1945) and yeast (Lindegren and Lindegren, 1947) that the inheritance of physiological differences has been worked out in greatest detail. Similar studies have been made in the higher plants, and for a few characters, such as reaction to length of day and the genetic control of the auxin mechanisms, fairly precise results have been obtained.

In any cross between two species, therefore, the inherent differences that allow them to fit into different habitats segregate in the same manner as morphological ones. The F_1 is as uniform as the parental species; the F_2 is highly variable. The preferences of first-generation hybrids are substantially alike and are more or less intermediate between those of the two parents. In succeeding hybrid generations or backcrosses these inherent differences recombine variously. Just as most of the hybrids of the second generation represent different recombinations of the morphological characters of the parents so that no two look exactly alike, so the habitat preferences of these same plants vary from individual to individual. Though they came from species that were each essentially uniform in their requirements for an optimum habitat, this second generation is made up of individuals each of which differs from the rest

in its requirements. The same is true of the backcrosses.
Just as they are *characterized morphologically* by individuals
that vary somewhat among themselves but as a whole are
fairly similar to their recurrent * parental species, so they
are *characterized physiologically* by individuals whose requirements are somewhat variable though as a whole are fairly
close to those of the parent to which they were backcrossed.

In nature, therefore, the problem of survival is very different for the first and for succeeding hybrid generations.
If two species inhabiting two different habitats are crossed
under natural conditions, the first hybrid generation can be
expected to survive if there are occasional intermediate
zones in which conditions as a whole are somewhat intermediate between that of the two habitats. All the individuals of the first hybrid generation are substantially alike,
differing no more among themselves than did the individuals
of the more variable parental species. Furthermore, as a
result of their hybridity, they ordinarily are vigorous and,
once established, may (depending on the degree of their
hybrid vigor) be more capable of maintaining themselves
than an ordinary nonhybrid. The progeny of these first-
generation hybrids, however, presents quite a different problem. Each of them prefers a slightly different habitat. Their
preferences as a whole run from something more or less like
that of one species, through a whole series of varying intermediate conditions, to something more or less like that of the
other parent.

Multiple habitats such as would be demanded if any considerable portion of the segregating hybrid generations were
to survive are seldom met with in nature. Even if complex
hybrid swarms are growing under natural conditions, a
repetition of the cross in an experimental garden reveals
whole groups of hybrids and backcrosses that were not found
in the wild population. They were missing not because such

---

* Following general usage by plant breeders, we shall refer to the
parental species to which the hybrid has been backcrossed for one or
more generations as the *recurrent* parental species.

zygotes were not formed, but because there was no "recombination habitat" in which they could survive. It is usually only through the intervention of man that such multiple habitats are even approximated. When he digs ditches, lumbers woodlands, builds roads, creates pastures, etc., man unconsciously brings about new combinations of light and moisture and soil conditions. At such time he may be said to "hybridize the habitat," and it is significant that many of the careful studies of hybridization in the field have been made in such areas. As to the way in which the same effects can under certain circumstances occur without the intervention of man, see Chapter 5, pp. 62 to 66.

Even where man has "hybridized the habitat," most of the new recombination habitats are fairly close to one of the original ones. In such areas, therefore, we may generally expect to find recombination plants closely resembling one of the parental species. The hybrids and backcrosses most likely to survive will be those very similar to one or the other of the parents. The restrictive effect of the environment will be to limit the results of hybridization in nature very largely to backcrosses. Among them, the environment will ordinarily give greatest preference to those backcrosses most like the recurrent species.

The greater the number of gene differences between the parents, the greater will be the number of special new habitats necessary for the segregates. Everything else being equal, we shall expect the lack of recombined habitats to be the stronger barrier, the greater the differentiation between two hybridizing entities.

If 2 hybridizing entities are differentiated by only 1 pair of genes affecting habitat preferences, the F_2 will demand only these 2 habitats and their intermediate condition. If there are 2 pairs of differentiating genes, we need 4 habitats; if there are 3 differences, we require 8. With only 10 such differences 1024 habitats are required; and with 20, over 1,000,000. Let us see exactly what these figures mean. Assuming no other barriers and no inherent disharmonies in the new recombinations, if the pairs of genes that fit 2 differentiated species each to its own distinctive habitats are no more than 20, the F_2 of this species cross will require over 1,000,000 kinds of habitat. With no more gene differences than 10 or 20, surely a conservative figure, they therefore require an impossibly large number of adjacent habitats if the recombinations are to be as well fitted to their situations as the parental species were to their 2.

As a crude example, let us consider the adjacent habitats in which one finds *Tradescantia subaspera* and *Tradescantia canaliculata* at home in the Ozark Plateau. The former grows in deep, rich woods at the foot of bluffs; the latter grows up above in full sun at the edge of the cliffs. We can list 3 of the outstanding differences between these 2 habitats as follows:

rich loam	rocky soil
deep shade	full sun
leaf-mold cover	no leaf-mold cover

Tradescantia canaliculata and *Tradescantia subaspera* are well-differentiated species; each is more closely related to several different species than to the other. Still, experiment has shown not only that they can be crossed readily by artificial means but also that they do cross abundantly when left to themselves in an experimental garden. Yet very few of the first-generation hybrids have been found in nature. The habitats of the 2 species are strikingly different in the Ozarks. There one seldom finds the intermediate habitat in which the hybrid is able to germinate and survive: This is a gravelly soil, partial shade with some bright sunlight, and a light covering of leaf mold. Imagine, however, the habitat that must be provided if we are to find in nature the second-generation recombinations which we obtain in the breeding plot. Making the example fantastically simpler than it really is and assuming that the 3 differences noted above are due to only 3 single-factor differences, we would find that our recombinations would even then require the following 6

new habitats (in addition to the various intermediary and
the parental ones):

rich loam	rich loam	rich loam
full sun	full sun	deep shade
no leaf mold	leaf mold	no leaf mold

rocky soil	rocky soil	rocky soil
deep shade	full sun	deep shade
leaf mold	leaf mold	no leaf mold

Imagine what would have to happen to any natural area
before such a set of variously intermediate habitats could be
provided! It has been very generally recognized that if hybrids are to survive we must have intermediate habitats for
them. It has not been emphasized, however, that, if anything beyond the first hybrid generation is to pull through,
we must have habitats not only that are intermediate but
also that present all possible recombinations of the contrasting differences of the original habitats. If the two species
differ in their response to light, soil, and moisture (and what
related species do not?), we must have varied recombinations of light, soil, and moisture for their hybrid descendants.
Only by a hybridization of the habitat can the hybrid recombinations be preserved in nature.

Seen in the light of the above argument, Riley's and
Viosca's detailed reports (see Chapter 1) on the irises of the
Mississippi Delta acquire new significance. They demonstrate a close connection between the treatment of the habitat and the number and kinds of hybrids that appeared.
Though the narrow French farms were as close together as
laboratory plots, nearly all the hybrids were concentrated
on one farm. The conspicuously segregating Colony H-1
was co-extensive with a small piece of wooded pasture that
had been repeatedly cut over and subjected to overpasturing.
The area in which the hybrids were found went right up to
the fence line and stopped there. Though irises were on the
neighboring farms, they were not hybrids. Colony H-2, on

the same farm, was in a spot that had been less radically disturbed, and it contained fewer individuals of obviously hybrid ancestry. Throughout the entire site, as a matter of fact, the degree of introgression was directly proportional to the disturbance of "natural conditions" by man and his domestic animals.

In general, therefore, the habitat exercises a tremendously -strong restriction upon hybridization between well-differentiated entities. Recombinations resembling the parental forms, and backcrosses resembling the parents, are at a strong selective advantage. The production of hybrid swarms is limited to particular times and places at which man or nature may have "hybridized the habitat." Even in many of these cases, as the previous ecological balance is restored, recombinations closely resembling the original parents will be those most likely to survive. The commonest end result of a hybrid swarm will be the introduction of a comparatively few genes from one species into the germplasm of another—in other words, introgression.

CHAPTER 3

The Genetic Basis
of Introgression

It is in general true that organisms which we believe to be closely related are most likely to be fertile with one another and that those which we believe to be distantly related are less so. On the whole, all the members of any one species are usually interfertile; closely related species are usually more difficult to hybridize, and their hybrids are only partially fertile; and it is ordinarily impossible to obtain hybrids between distinct genera. To the man in the street, and sometimes even to the research biologist, hybrids between species have come to be thought of as something exceptional and contrary to the laws of nature. But as anyone can find out who has the patience to look into the extensive literature on the subject, these generalizations are only broadly true; they summarize an average condition. Fertility of a degree that will permit ready gene exchange is usually to be found only between closely related species. There are, however, numerous exceptions in each direction.

At the one extreme there are exceptional genera like Drosophila in which species are difficult or impossible to hybridize even though they are so closely related that they can be distinguished only by specialists and by them only with difficulty. At the other extreme there are genera like Aquilegia and Narcissus in which all the species, even the most diverse, can be hybridized with each other, and (aside from the special effects produced by polyploidy) in which the hybrids will be partially fertile. In the Orchidaceae, hybrids combining the germplasm of three or more genera are bred on a commercial scale as ornamental plants (Cattlyea, Laelia, Brassovala, and Odontoglossum, Miltonia, Cochlioda). The Laelio-Brasso-Cattlyeas can also be hybridized and yield partially fertile progeny with species of Epidendrum and of Sophronitis. The Milto-Ondontiodas similarly may be crossed with species of the genus Oncidium. Some of the widest known crosses have been produced artificially between exceedingly distinct genera in the grass family. Mangelsdorf and Reeves produced hybrids of Zea with Tripsacum, genera so distinct that the homologous parts of the inflorescences in the two are still matters of dispute. Hybrids between sugar canes (Saccharum) and other grasses having been demonstrated, Dr. Janaki-Ammal attempted a whole series of intergeneric crosses. She succeeded (1941, 1942) in obtaining hybrids and second-generation descendants between Saccharum and Erianthus and between Saccharum and Imperata. She even obtained weak F_1's between sugar cane (Saccharum) and maize (Zea). Other sugar-cane breeders produced useful crosses between Sorghum and sugar cane and between sugar cane and Narenga. These amazing results were first received with considerable scepticism, but Janaki-Ammal's detailed descriptions and photographs left room for little doubt. Similar results have since been obtained by other sugar-cane breeders.

One of the widest fertile crosses known occurred in England (Osborn, 1941), where the Monterey Cypress, *Cupressus macrocarpa*, and the Yellow Cedar from the Pacific Coast of North America, *Chamaecyparis nootkatensis*, were grown near each other on a private estate and both reached fruiting size. Among the seedlings that were raised from *both* parents were a few which differed from their siblings to such a degree that they were noticed and kept track of. As they developed, both sets were found to be intermediate between Cupressus and Chamaecyparis, and the two sets were essentially alike. There was then little doubt that an intergeneric hybrid had occurred. Specimens of the hybrid (known horticulturally as *Cupressocyparis Leylandii*) have been grown to fruiting age and seedlings have been raised from them, demonstrating that under certain conditions gene exchange is possible between these distinct genera.

There are not at the present time enough experimental data even for a rough estimate of the possible frequency of interspecific and intergeneric crosses in different groups of organisms. For various reasons it has been simpler to attempt species and generic crossing on a large scale among the higher plants than among the insects or the vertebrates. The number of wide crosses known among the higher plants might equally well be due to a wider tolerance of such miscegenation there, or to the much lesser number of artificial crosses that have been attempted among the vertebrates and insects, for all we know at the present time. The fact that species hybrids and semifertile generic hybrids have been so frequently obtained among the fishes looks suggestive but can scarcely be taken as conclusive. Aside from the higher plants, the one group of organisms the largest numbers of which have been successfully raised in captivity is the fishes, and it is among them that the largest number of vertebrate crosses permitting gene exchange between distinct genera has been reported.

For the higher plants the actual experimental evidence is more extensive than many biologists realize. From the time when Camerarius first announced that the higher plants were sexual in nature, until the early days of genetics, a whole series of investigators pursued the subject, first establishing in the face of stiff opposition (Zirkle, 1935) the fact that such hybrids could really be made, and then launching an attempt to summarize and analyze the results of these crosses. The total number of precise scientific controlled experiments in this era was staggering. Von Gärtner, the outstanding of these hybridizers, worked with around 700 species. He attempted more than 10,000 controlled, recorded crosses and produced 250 different hybrids.

When the possibilities of hybridization became apparent, it was carried on extensively by amateurs and horticulturists for practical purposes. This work still continues. While some scientists were still debating whether intergeneric crosses such as those made by Janaki-Ammal were a scientific possibility in the Gramineae, the sugar-cane industry was producing them on a commercial scale in its breeding fields. If one will but leaf through such a comprehensive catalogue of horticultural plant material as Rehder's *Manual of Cultivated Trees and Shrubs*, he will gain some idea of the number of interspecific and intergeneric crosses that have been achieved. Unfortunately, such a compendium gives a very incomplete picture. It says nothing at all about the even larger number of crosses that were attempted and did not succeed.

A modern summary of the evidence of hybridization is badly needed. One was last brought together by Focke (1881) in his classical *Die Pflanzen Mischlinge*. His general conclusions would find even stronger support from the evidence that has accumulated since his day. "Der Grad der morphologischen und der physiologischen Verschiedenheit entsprechen einander häufig ziemlich genau, doch gibt es auch Beispiele, in denen dies durchaus, *nicht* der Fall ist." (The degree of morphological difference is usually closely parallel to that of the physiological difference, yet there are examples in which this is certainly *not* the case.)

To summarize: The production of hybrids fertile enough to lead to gene exchange is in general common within species, less common between closely related species, and rare (but by no means unknown) between entities that by all other criteria are distinct genera. In a very few cases hybrids have been produced between genera not even closely related. Only among the plants do we have enough of both positive and negative evidence to generalize upon this point. There are some preliminary indications (fish, tree frogs, cattle relatives) that similar wide crosses may be found to be as common among the vertebrates, when as high a proportion of such possibilities have been experimentally attempted.

Since the times of the early hybridizers it has been known that, though many interspecific hybridizations give similar results, there were a considerable number of exceptional cases, such as true-breeding hybrids, segregating first-generation hybrids, sterile *intra*specific crosses, etc. Modern cytology has shown the special features that produce these exceptions and now includes all these seeming exceptions under one general theory. We shall restrict the following discussion to the commonest and most general kinds of hybrids, those which (in Darlington's terminology) come from unlike parents and give rise to unlike offspring. The general results of such hybridizations have again been known since the times of Koelretuer and Von Gärtner (Plates 4 and 5). The first hybrid (F_1) generation is uniform, sometimes strikingly so. Aside from differences due to the extreme vigor that tends to characterize such hybrids, it is morphologically intermediate between the two parents. On the other hand, the second generation (F_2) characteristically varies (Plate 4) from individual to individual. If raised by the tens or by the hundreds, seldom are there two individuals with exactly the same combination of parental characteristics. In general, a large F_2 can be shown to pass from a few recombinations very similar to one of the parents, to a great variety of intermediates—the majority of which are fairly similar to the F_1—to a relatively few individuals very much like the other parent.

If the F_1 is backcrossed to the two parental species, each of these backcross generations varies from individual to individual, though not so markedly as the F_2. In such backcrosses (Plate 5) usually a few individuals are almost indistinguishable from the recurrent parent (i.e., the one to which they have been backcrossed), and a large number are in various ways intermediate between this parent and the F_1. A few will be rather similar to the F_1 itself. If any of these first backcrosses are again crossed back to the same parent the resulting progeny vary even less among themselves and are in general very similar to the recurrent parent. After a succession of 5 or 6 such backcrosses they usually become indistinguishable from the recurrent parent.

Genetics has given us a sound theoretical basis for interpreting these results. The multiple-factor hypothesis explains them in the following way: Let us suppose that the differences between two hybridizing entities are conditioned by a single factor. If there is no dominance, the condition for one parent may be written as AA, and that for the other parent as $A'A'$, and the F_1 hybrid will be AA' and intermediate. In the F_2 these differences will segregate in a ratio of $1\ AA : 2\ AA' : 1\ A'A'$. If the differences between the two parents are due to two genes A vs. A' and B vs. B', then again the hybrid $AA'BB'$ will be intermediate, but this time in the F_2 we shall have a much more complicated segregation. The genotypes and their ratios will be:

		NUMBER OF (') GENES
1	$AABB$	0
2	$AA'BB$	1
2	$AABB'$	1
4	$AA'BB'$	2
1	$AAB'B'$	2
2	$AA'B'B'$	3
1	$A'A'BB$	2
2	$A'A'BB'$	3
1	$A'A'B'B'$	4

Now for the purposes of illustration, we consider the extremely simple case of a difference between 2 parents that is equally due to 2 pairs of genes, A vs. A' and B vs. B'. Let us suppose (to take an example simpler than any for which we yet have experimental evidence) that the difference between the 2 parents lies entirely in leaf length and that this difference is 4 units. If we diagram the short-leaved parent as $AABB$ and the long-leaved one as $A'A'B'B'$, and if, as we have supposed, the length difference is borne equally by the 2 gene pairs and is without dominance effects, then the F_1, $AA'BB'$, will be 2 units larger than the small-leaved parent. An additional unit of leaf length will have been contributed by A', and another unit by B'. In a similar way we can assign length values to the 9 possible genotypes in the F_2. They will all go into 5 size classes, i.e., (1) those with no additional units for length, (2) those with 1 additional unit, (3) those with 2, (4) those with 3, and (5) those with 4.

The $AAB'B'$ genotype, for instance, has 2 genes for additional length. It will produce leaves of the same size class as do $A'A'BB$ and $AA'BB'$, each of which also has 2 genes from the larger parent. If we collect the various genotypes into the 5 size classes and summarize our expectation, we obtain the following:

0 genes for additional length				1
1 " " " "				4
2 " " " "				6
3 " " " "				4
4 " " " "				1
				—
				16

In other words, we shall expect about one sixteenth of the second-generation hybrids to be as small as the small parent, and another sixteenth to be as large as the large parent. About one quarter of the population will be intermediate between the small parent and the F_1, and another quarter will in turn be intermediate between the large parent and F_1. More than a third of the second-generation plants ($\frac{6}{16}$) will be the same length as the F_1.

In Table 2 are shown the expected distributions for 3 gene differences and for 4 gene differences and the general formulae for any number of differences. It will be noted that with an increase in the number of genes affecting a character the number of possible genotypes increases exponentially, as does all the possible number of intermediates between the two parental extremes.

As we consider larger and larger numbers of independent genes all affecting the same character, the chances of getting individuals that resemble either parent become less and less. With only 10 genes there is only 1 chance in 1,000,000 of getting an F_2 plant like one of the parents; with 20 independent genes the chances are 1 in 1,000,000,000,000. At the same time the chances of producing plants with values close to those of the F_1 become greater and greater.

In the same way we may consider theoretical expectations among the backcrosses. As the numbers of genes affecting a character increase, there is again an exponential increase in the number of possible intermediates but at a lower rate than in the F_2. The chances of producing a backcross exactly similar to the recurrent parent also become exponentially less, but again at a lower rate. With 10 genes there is still about 1 chance in 1000 ($\frac{1}{1024}$) of obtaining the same gene combination as the original parent.

It will be noticed that the ratio between the expectation of recovering the parental type in a backcross and in an F_2 is an exponential one. Since the chances of recovering the parental gene combination in an F_2 are $\frac{1}{4}^n$ and in a backcross are $\frac{1}{2}^n$, the parental type is 2^n times as likely to occur in a backcross as in an F_2. Where n equals the number of gene differences, with 5 gene differences, the chances of recovering the parental type in a backcross are 30 times what they would be in an F_2; with 10 gene differences they rise to over 1000 times, and with 20 gene differences to over 1,000,-000. Since in species crosses we are dealing with large numbers of gene differences, this is a significant point. The greater the gene differences between two hybridizing entities, the exponentially greater are the comparative chances of reassembling the parental gene combination in a backcross.

The explanation as outlined above is, of course, highly theoretical. It assumes that all genes have equal effects, that none of them are dominant, and that there are no special factors affecting the randomness of segregation, of fertilization, of gametic survival, and of zygotic survival. All such complications are known, but before we can consider them and their effects we must understand the basic genetics of large numbers of multiple factors.

From theoretical genetics, therefore, following the argument outlined above and using the basic formulae of Table 2, we can expect that with a large number of independent genes such as would be found in a species cross, and with no further complicating factors, the F_2 would be composed of individuals no two of which would be exactly alike but most of which would be intermediate between the two parents. Recombinations somewhat resembling either parent would be very much in the minority. In a similar way with a large number of independent factors all the backcrosses would tend to be different from each other and for the most part intermediate between the F_1 and the recurrent parent. Individuals closely resembling this parent (as in the F_2) would be in the minority but not so strikingly as in the F_2.

If we study the curve $(1 : 2 : 1)^n$ we find that, with an increasing number of independent genes responsible for the differences between the two species, there is a great increase in the proportion of the F_2 plants that are about as intermediate as was the F_1. At the same time the number of different genotypes that can produce this intermediate condition also rises enormously. With a very large number of independent genes we expect an F_2 that phenotypically is not very different from the F_1 yet that genotypically is tremendously variable from plant to plant.

So far we have considered the kinds of results that would be obtained by many independent genes all affecting the same character. Actually, of course, such results are absolutely impossible in any plant or animal known to science. The germplasm is not made up of tiny independent units. It is organized into chromosomes—long, narrow, threadlike protein aggregations with longitudinal differentiation of the germinal material. The genes in any one chromosome are not free to assort at random with each other. A certain amount of recombination is possible, the exact amount depending on how much crossing over takes place at the reduction division and on the extent to which crossovers tend to be localized. In any case, however, the gene recombinations that can be achieved within a chromosome pair are an almost infinitesimal fraction of what could be obtained with the same number of completely independent genes.

To find out the effect of linkage in a cross between two species differing by a large number of genes, let us first consider a hypothetical limiting case. Suppose the two species differ by 50 genes and that these gene differences are more or less uniformly distributed through 10 pairs of chromosomes. If there were no recombination within any of the

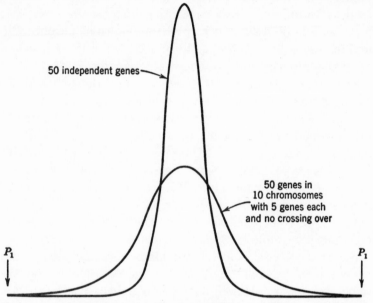

Fig. 1. F_2 frequency curves for a character controlled by 50 genes all equal in effect, with and without linkage.

chromosomes (and though such a case is certainly extreme it is not unknown experimentally), each of the chromosomes would behave like a giant gene. Its 5 genes would always segregate simultaneously. The segregation of 50 genes each on a separate chromosome would follow the curve $(1 : 2 : 1)^{50}$. Their segregation if they were in 10 chromosomes with no crossing over would be represented by $(1 : 2 : 1)^{10}$. If in the first case we give each segregating gene pair a value of 1 unit in determining the difference in the character in question, then in the second example each of the chromosomes is behaving like a giant gene of 5 units of value. The results to be expected by these two hypothetical cases are compared in Fig. 1. It will be seen that they are exactly the same general type of curve. The effects of linkage are greatly to increase the chances of getting F_2 recombinations very similar to the parental species and greatly to decrease the percentage of segregants more or less similar to the F_1.

With linkage there is one chance in a thousand of obtaining an F_2 individual with the same combination of genes as one of the parents. Without linkage, for the same number of genes the chances would be only one in a million, million, million, million, million (10^{-30}). In other words, if we grew several hundred F_2 plants of each of these two hypothetical

TABLE 2

No. of Gene Differences between Parents	F_1 Formulae	No. of Genotypes in F_2	Frequency of Distribution of F_2's	Proportion of F_2's Equaling Either Parent	No. of Genotypes in First Backcross	Frequency Distribution of Backcross	Proportion of Backcross Equaling Recurrent Parent
1	AA'	3	1:2:1	$\frac{1}{4}$	2	1:1	$\frac{1}{2}$
2	$AA'BB'$	9	1:4:6:4:1	$\frac{1}{16}$	4	1:2:1	$\frac{1}{4}$
3	$AA'BB'CC'$	27	1:6:15:20:15:6:1	$\frac{1}{64}$	8	1:3:3:1	$\frac{1}{8}$
4	$AA'BB'CC'DD'$	81	1:8:28:56:70:56:28:8:1	$\frac{1}{256}$	16	1:4:6:4:1	$\frac{1}{16}$
N		3^N	$(1:2:1)^N$	$\frac{1}{4}^N$	2^N	$(1:1)^N$	$\frac{1}{2}^N$

cases, for those with the genes in 10 chromosomes we would expect several plants closely resembling each parent, and there is a very slight chance we might get one exactly like one of the parents. In the second case the chances of any such recombination (10^{-30}) are too remote for most human minds to grasp. We could not possibly expect, among our sample of a few hundred individuals, any recombination resembling either parent at all closely.

Up to this point our exposition has been concerned with relatively simple cases of a multiple-factor difference affecting a single character (such as leaf length, for instance). In nature, of course, we never meet with such simple cases. Species do not differ from one another just in leaf length and nothing else, but in various characters. Some of these differences are clearly multifactorial in their genetic basis; others, such as flower color or color pattern, are much simpler and result largely from differences in one or a few pairs of genes.

The genetics of a species cross is, therefore, a far more complicated subject than those examples we have been considering. Both the basic data and the basic theory are challengingly difficult. To catalogue in their entirety the simultaneous changes in a whole set of characters in an F_2 population, presenting an overall picture of the extent to which each character is independent of the variation in each of the others, is a complex task. No such body of data has yet been published for any species cross. Nor do we yet have a generalized theoretical presentation in genetic formulae, demonstrating the effects of large numbers of genes, organized in linkage groups, in hybrid and in backcross populations. Considering its theoretical and its practical importance, a thorough exposition of hybrid segregation in finite and in infinite populations is badly needed. To determine the overall effects of all the gene differences in all the chromosomes upon all the characters of successive hybrid generations, making due allowances for the effects of linkage and of finite populations, is almost beyond the power of the human mind. But because it is so difficult it is a challenging subject. In the following pages we shall not present any such generalized theory but shall attempt to determine (one at a time) the effects of those general forces that operate in all species crosses. Of these the most universal is linkage, and we shall try to estimate its cohesive effect upon the extent of character recombination and upon the comparative frequencies of different types of recombinations. We shall then summarize briefly the special forces that operate in some species crosses but not in others.

Before considering the theoretical basis of character recombination in the F_2, let us review the facts on the subject. It has already been mentioned that, except in certain exceptional cases, the F_1 of a cross between well-marked varieties, or between species, is highly uniform, whereas the F_2 is extremely variable. These two contrasting generations, the one so outstandingly uniform, the other so outstandingly variable, have caught the imaginations of nearly all those who have worked with them. The hybridizers have been so intrigued by this contrast that they have made little or no effort to catalogue and analyze the variation in F_2 populations. There does not seem to be a single published paper in which any attempt was made to determine whether the recombinations of the F_2 were infinite in their variety or occurred by the scores, by the hundreds, or by the thousands. From most of the descriptions in published papers one would gather that the number of recombinations were infinite; a little research in the tables accompanying these papers will show that a few hundred individuals, at the most, were under consideration. Yet it is quite simple to demonstrate (Anderson, unpublished) that in any such cross the numbers of recombinations are distinctly finite. It is possible to determine for any particular cross the numbers of F_2 individuals that must be grown before one has a good chance of obtaining two individuals essentially similar.

In one published case (Anderson, 1939b) a pioneer attempt was made to compare the recombination of the F_2 with the recombinations that might have been expected if there had been no restrictions of any sort upon complete recombination. "In *Nicotiana alata* $\times$ *N. Langsdorffii*, if we consider only the differences in tube length, in the lobing index, in style length, and in limb width, the recombinations obtained are only $\frac{1}{64}$ of the kinds of recombinations which might be obtained with free assortment. These four characters, however, represent only a few of many differences which might be considered between *N. alata* and *N. Langsdorffii*. It is, therefore, certain that the recombinations which we have obtained are only an insignificant fraction of the recombinations possible under free assortment.

"To a non-mathematical mind this may seem too strong a statement. When the data are presented, as for the most part they necessarily must be in terms of the recombination

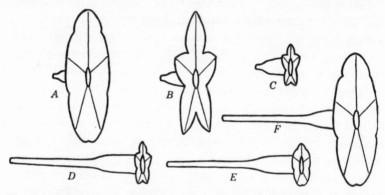

FIG. 2. Extreme recombinations to be expected in the F₂ between *Nicotiana Langsdorffii* and *N. alata* if there were no restrictions upon the recombination of corolla length, limb width, and lobing of the corolla. The letters refer to Fig. 4.

of two characters at a time, it takes a peculiar sort of geometric imagination to see that the proportion of actual recombinations to total recombinations becomes increasingly smaller as more characters are considered. Anyone who has examined second generations or back-crosses of species hybrids will have been so impressed by their variability that it will be difficult for him to accept the conclusion that such a mélange is only a small fraction of total recombination. For such biologists, and as a sort of graphical summary of all the data, figures 2 and 3 have been prepared. In figure 2 are illustrated the extreme types of corollas wich might be expected in the second generation if there were free recombination of tube length, limb width and lobing. In figure 3 are shown the closest approaches to these extremes which were actually observed among 347 F₂ plants. In figure 4 these same data are combined into a three-way correlation diagram showing the relation between total recombination for these three characters and the actual recombinations obtained in the experiment. A comparison of figures 2 and 3 with figure 4 will show that the mathematical deductions are indeed correct. The second generation extremes which at first

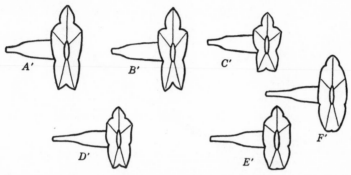

FIG. 3. Actual extreme recombinations, diagrammed to scale, obtained in a large F₂ between *N. Langsdorffii* and *N. alata*. *A'* is the closest approach obtained to the theoretical extreme *A* of Fig. 2, *B'* the closest to *B*, etc. The letters refer to Fig. 4.

seemed so variable become impressively uniform when compared to the imaginary recombinations of figure 2." (Anderson, 1939*b*).

THE RECOMBINATION SPINDLE

These data demonstrate that the recombinations of the F₂, however manifold they may seem, are in reality but a narrow segment of the total imaginable recombinations of the parental species. If we think of all the characters of one species being represented at one of the apices of a multidimensional cube and all the characters of the other species at the opposite apex, then the recombinations that we get in the F₂ form a narrow spindle through the center of the cube. In morphological language, though we have a great variety of recombinations, they can all be summarized as a general trend from recombinations more or less like one of the parental species, through those much like the F_1, to those more or less like the other parental species. In the following chapter, in considering the effects in later generations, we

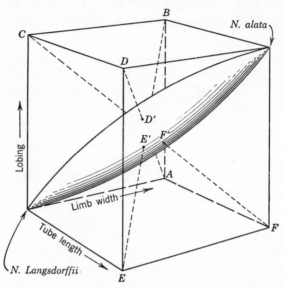

Fig. 4. The "recombination spindle" of *Nicotiana Langsdorffii* × *N. alata*. The theoretical recombinations, *A, B, C, D, E*, and *F*, of Fig. 2 would be at six corners of the cube of expectations. Tube length is measured on one axis, limb width on another, and lobing on the third. The recombinations form a spindle extending diagonally across the cube. On its surface are the actual extreme recombinations (*D', E'*, etc.), which are diagrammed to scale in Fig. 3.

shall have occasion to refer repeatedly to this "recombination spindle."

A theoretical consideration of what we might expect in hybrid populations brings us to exactly the same conclusions as did the experimental evidence from Nicotiana and the practical experience of plant breeders: There are strong cohesive forces within the germplasm. Although the germplasm may well be made up of unit genes (as most geneticists suppose), it is far from being pulverized. If each gene were on a tiny separate chromosome and the germplasm was composed of hundreds or thousands of such units, then we might get complete recombination of specific differences in hybrid populations. Germplasms, however, are not constructed in that way or in anything like that way. The genes are carried in long, protein, threadlike units, the chromosomes. Within each differing chromosome pair in a hybrid nucleus, only a very limited amount of exchange is possible. When crossing over does take place between sister chromosomes, leading to new intrachromosomal recombinations, the sister chromosomes are each longitudinally bipartite. At each point of exchange (chiasma) one thread (chromatid) of each exchanges with one thread of the other, leaving the other two threads in their original conditions. Gene exchange is, therefore, only half of what had been supposed on cruder hypotheses of crossing over.

The effects of basic chromosome structure upon specific and racial cohesion are of importance because they are universal and because in the aggregate they are powerful, much more powerful than might be expected without precise calculations. They are universal in that, with the exception of such organisms as bacteria (for which the evidence is still inconclusive), all germplasms in both plant and animal kingdoms have their genes in chromosomes, which (molecularly) are long, threadlike structures. The cohesive effects of a germplasm organized in this fashion are therefore always at work. From the very beginnings of differentiation between two varieties to the point where distinct genera may very occasionally cross with each other, these inherent forces of germinal cohesion are active, generation after generation. When two species hybridize, in each successive hybrid generation and in each successive backcross these forces come into play in every reduction division.

The aggregate magnitude of the specific and racial cohesion resulting from linkage is based on the fact that specific differences are the sum of all the differences between the species. Gene by gene, or chromosome sector by chromosome sector, the cohesive effect of long, threadlike germplasms is not very great. If we were to consider only three or four genes, the cohesive force imposed by protein chains is only of the order of 2/3 of the recombining that might occur without any such restraint. Species differences, however, are not matters of one or two genes; they are based upon a great many gene differences—certainly scores of them, perhaps hundreds, scattered all along the length of the chromosomes. The total cohesive effect of chain proteins in a species cross, therefore, becomes 2/3 of 2/3 of 2/3 of 2/3 $\cdots$. If the number of genes is large this reaches a staggering sum. As we shall show below, the total effect of these forces on the aggregate of all the differences in the germplasm is enormous. Its magnitude will vary with the number of genes concerned, with the frequency of chiasmata, and with the number of chromosomes, but it must always be high. We can grasp its general comparative magnitude if we consider two hypothetical limiting cases. Let us suppose that we have 2 species, *orientalis* and *occidentalis*, whose essential differences are due to 100 genes. If these genes were all aggregated in one big chromosome, with such strongly localized chiasmata that there was no effective interchange at meiosis, we could then have only 3 kinds of hybrid offspring, those with 2 chromosomes of *orientalis*, those with 2 of *occidentalis* and those with 1 of each. As our other limiting case, let us suppose that the genes were in 100 separate chromosomes. The possible number of hybrid gene recombinations would then be 3^{100}.

These are the two hypothetical limiting cases. Neither is realized in nature. The male Drosophila is, however, very close to complete linkage. There are only 4 chromosomes, and there is in the male no effective crossing over within any one of the 4. In other organisms more recombination is achieved. The larger the number of chromosomes, and the greater the number of chiasmata per chromosome, and the less localization there is in the points at which chiasmata are bound to occur, the greater will be the recombination. It will readily be seen, however, that, even if we take those organisms with the largest numbers of chromosomes, the most chiasmata, and the least localized chiasmata, we are still much closer to the hypothetical extreme of complete linkage than we are to the other extreme of no linkage. Even under the least effective conditions, the fact that the genes are situated in long, protein structures has a powerful effect upon specific and racial cohesion.

Linkage has two restrictive effects upon recombination. It limits the numbers of types of different recombinations that can be achieved in any one generation, irrespective of population size. It also affects the frequency with which any particular recombination type can occur. Recombinations requiring a linkage break will, of course, appear with reduced frequencies. In dealing with multiple-factor characters where very large numbers of genes are concerned, the frequency of practically every recombination is affected. The effect of linkage upon frequencies had been apparent to many geneticists and was specifically discussed by D. F. Jones in 1920. "Two factors in each chromosome so spaced as to have 10 per cent breaks in the linkage with each other would necessitate 20^{20} individuals in the segregating generation to have an even chance of securing the one plant desired. This number of corn plants would require an area roughly 3,700,000,-000,000 times the area of the United States." (Jones, 1920).

The restriction imposed even upon populations infinite in size was first pointed out by Anderson in 1939. The following discussion has been slightly condensed from the original accounts (Anderson, 1939a and b):

The restraint of linkages imposes severe restrictions upon the kinds of gene combinations that are possible with any frequency. When all the loci of a germplasm are considered, this restriction is as important as that imposed upon frequencies and runs into figures of astronomical magnitude. Some notion of its greatness may be gained by considering recombination in a single crossover segment of the germplasm. Let us take the simple example of a short chromosome in which there is regularly a single crossover. Let us further suppose that in the 2 species, or races, which are to be crossed, there are 10 pairs of gene differences within this chromosome. This seems a conservative number for a length of germplasm which might well be 50 units long genetically and made up of 200 or more genes.

In the gametes of the first-generation hybrid, as a result of 4-strand crossing over, one half of the gametes will have one crossed-over section in this chromosome and the other half will have none. The number of crossovers per chromosome will be increased the same way in each generation: Double crossovers will not be possible until the F_2 generation forms its gametes, triple crossovers until the F_3, etc. In each generation one half the gametes will acquire an extra crossover, one half will continue the previous number. The number of crossovers per gamete and the proportions of each kind of gamete can therefore be obtained from expanding $(\frac{1}{2} + \frac{1}{2})^n$, in which n equals the number of hybrid generations. For the 10 gene pairs under consideration complete recombination cannot be attained until gametes are produced in which all 9 breaks between the original sets of 10 differing gene pairs have occurred. To obtain such a gamete will require a minimum of 9 hybrid generations, and even then these gametes may be expected only once in 2^9 ($= 512$). It will require twice as many hybrid generations before gametes of this degree of recombination will be in the majority.

A more precise estimate of the hindrance to recombination can be obtained by considering the ratio of the possible gene combinations in the germ cells of F_1 to random combination. With 3 pairs of differing loci, abc/ABC, there can be a crossover between the a locus and the b locus and between the b and the c. Each of these will permit two recombinations, viz., aBC, Abc, and abC, ABc. The total number of recombinations will therefore be equal to twice the number of gene abutments or $2(n - 1)$, in which n equals the number of differing gene pairs. With the two original combinations the total number of kinds of gametes will be $2n$. Since the total number of possible combinations of unlinked genes is given by 2^n, the ratio we are seeking will be $2n/2^n$. For 3 pairs of gene differences this becomes $3/4$; for 4 pairs $1/2$; for 10 pairs $10/512$, or less than 2 per cent.

Since the same principle will be operating in every crossover region (tempered only by the occurrence of multiple crossing over), the total hindrance in the entire germplasm will be enormous. An estimate can be obtained by considering the not impossible case of an organism that regularly has a single chiasma in each chromosome. For such an organism the ratio of the possible kinds of gametes to the total number of recombinations will be $(2n/2^n)^N$, in which n equals the numbers of differing loci per chromosome and N is the number of pairs of chromosomes. For even such a slight difference as 4 genes per chromosome and with only 6 pairs of chromosomes this ratio becomes $1/64$. For 10 gene differences per chromosome and with 10 pairs of chromosomes it becomes $(10/512)^{10}$, or roughly less than 1 in 100,000,000,-000,000,000.

It should be emphasized that this restriction is independent of the size of the F_2 and constitutes an absolute *upper* limit to gene recombination in that generation. The ratio $(10/512)^{10}$, inconceivably small though it may be, represents the fraction of the total recombinations which could be achieved in a population of infinite size. This is a number so large that it has little meaning to the human mind.

A graphical example of the recombinations of one chromosome was worked out in detail (Anderson, 1939*b*). With a few minor corrections, this is presented here as Plate 2. The figure shows all the possible recombinations in the F_2. With complete recombination the entire quadrangular coordinate would have been covered and the possible recombinations would have formed a square instead of a diagonal spindle.

The diagram is restricted to a single pair of chromosomes differing in 6 essential genes affecting 2 different characters. The question of frequencies is not considered. The diagram

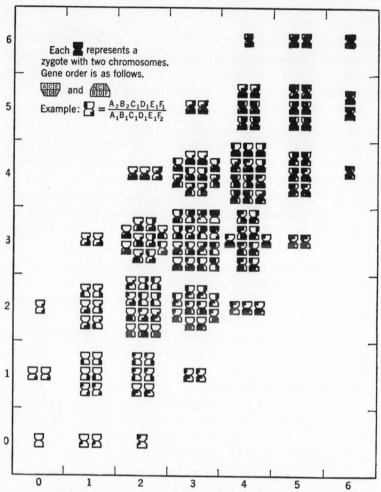

PLATE 2. Diagram showing all the possible recombinations which could be obtained in an F_2 for a pair of segregating chromosomes ($A_1B_1C_1D_1E_1F_1$, diagrammed in white, vs. $A_2B_2C_2D_2E_2F_2$, diagrammed in black). Each dumbbell represents a different genotype and diagrams the two chromosomes of which it is made up, one above and one below. The genes A, C, and E affect a character whose values are measured on the horizontal axis. The genes B, D, and F affect another character whose values are measured on the vertical axis. All the possible recombinations in such an F_2 are shown to form a "recombination spindle" passing from the corner $(0, 0)$ that was characteristic of one species to the corner $(6, 6)$ that was characteristic of the other. Comparative frequencies of the recombinations not considered. Further explanation in the text.

40

illustrates all the F_2 genotypes that would be possible in an F_2 of infinite size. The F_1 is furthermore considered to be perfectly fertile, and no structural differences affecting pairing or crossing over have been assumed.

Factorially, the 2 parental chromosome types are assumed to be a_1, b_1, c_1, d_1, e_1, f_1 and a_2, b_2, c_2, d_2, e_2, f_2. The factors in boldface type, **b**, **d**, and **f**, affect one character, and a, c, and e affect the other. The species diagrammed in white is supposed to have a minimum value for each of the 2 characters, and the species diagrammed in black is supposed to owe its greater magnitude to the equal and additive effect of each of the 6 genes for which it is homozygous. (These assumptions are not necessary to the theory, but they make for a simpler and more readily understandable diagram.) Each dumbbell-shaped figure in the diagram denotes a single F_2 genotype, black representing genes from the large species and white those from the small. As shown at the upper left of the diagram, the upper half of the "dumbbell" represents one of the chromosomes, the lower half the sister chromosome. The chromosome is diagrammatically represented in the compact zigzag arrangement $\overset{a}{\searrow}_{\mathbf{b}}\overset{c}{\nearrow\searrow}_{\mathbf{d}}\overset{e}{\nearrow\searrow}_{\mathbf{f}}$ so that the 3 factors a, c, and e affecting one character are pushed towards the top, and the other 3 (**b**, **d**, and **f**) are pushed towards the bottom. The smaller species is given a base value of 0 for each character. The larger species, by definition, will therefore carry 3 units of increase in each of its chromosomes, for each character, and its value on the diagram will be 6 for each.

The diagram is for a short chromosome which regularly has one chiasma and only one, so that only single crossovers are possible. If the 6 genes were in separate chromosomes, 64 types of gametes would be possible. Linkage (wholly aside from its effect on frequencies) reduces the number of kinds to 12.

Even in populations of infinite size, therefore, the effect of linkage upon recombination types is very great. If scores or hundreds of gene differences are concerned in species crosses (as has been assumed by those geneticists who have made serious attempts to obtain data on this difficult point), then it is a force so great as to require scores of generations of controlled breeding before it could be completely nullified. In natural populations the effects of linkage upon gene frequencies are equally important, and they will be discussed in the following chapter.

Were the science of cytogenetics further advanced it might be instructive to calculate the cohesive effect of linkage in a set of limiting cases. We are still at the point, however, where we have to make too many assumptions in lieu of actual data. We do not have any exact information (even exact estimates) as to the number of gene differences between species. As important as data on gene number are data on chiasma frequency and localization. Chiasmata are the result of exchange between homologous chromosomes at the reduction division. The greater the chiasma frequency, the larger is the number of units in which the germplasm may be shuffled, and the less is the cohesive effect. Quite as important for our purpose are data on chiasma localization. From cytological observation we know in a rough way that in some species chiasmata are highly localized; that is, they tend very strongly to occur in certain parts of the chromosomes. In other species no such tendency is clearly manifest, and they are said (by cytologists) to occur at random. For a precise computation of the cohesive effect of linkage we need to know just how randomized the chiasmata are. The more they tend to be localized, the less variation there will be in gene combinations between sister germ cells and the stronger will be the cohesive force of linkage. Chiasma number determines the number of segregating blocks in the germplasm. Localization determines how closely the blocks produced by any one pollen mother cell of a plant resemble those produced by its sister cells.

Among the higher plants the available data would suggest that an average condition might be something like 12 pairs of chromosomes, with 2 to 3 chiasmata per chromosome and with at least a slight tendency for these chiasmata to occur more frequently in certain parts of the chromosomes. Under such conditions, with about 100 gene differences between 2 species, the cohesive force of multiple-factor linkage would be in the neighborhood of 1/500,000 of free recombination.

CHARACTER ASSOCIATION AS A CRITERION OF HYBRIDITY

New and powerful criteria for the analysis of hybridization under natural conditions were offered by the demonstration that all the multiple-factor characters of an organism are linked with each other so strongly that in species crosses it would take scores of generations of directed breeding to break all the linkages. Two criteria were pointed out specifically in 1939 (Anderson, *loc. cit.*, p. 692). "1. The intermediacy of separate characters will be correlated. Hybrids intermediate in one character will tend to be intermediate in others. Hybrids which are most like either parent in any one character will tend to resemble that parent in all other characters. 2. Variation between individuals will lessen as parental character combinations are approached." The application of these criteria (and similar criteria based on multiple-factor linkage) make it possible to take most arguments concerning natural hybridization out of the domain of opinion and into that of measurement. If those who are inclined to argue about the importance or nonimportance of hybridization under natural conditions would only gather precise data on character recombination in natural populations, we should have the facts on which sound opinions could be based. By such methods as those demonstrated in Chapter 6, it is now possible to procure critical data from variable populations, which will demonstrate conclusively the role of hybridization in that particular population. It may be well, therefore, to give a detailed discussion of the theoretical basis for these criteria.

The first step in the analysis of any highly variable population is to discover at least two characters that are varying and to devise means for measuring this variation objectively. They should, if at all possible, be characters with no transparent dependency upon each other or upon a common factor. Corolla length, leaf length, and internode length, for instance, might be expected to vary more or less together; the same influences that produced a longer leaf on one plant might well produce larger flowers and longer internodes on the stem.

The second step is to score a number of individual plants simultaneously for these two characters and then to plot the results as a scatter diagram. Let us suppose that in such a population we have found leaves to vary from glabrous to highly pubescent and the flower color to range from very light to quite dark. Having turned each of these two characters into a set of objective grades and scored 25 plants for both, we then produce a scatter diagram that shows graphically the extent to which variation in flower color is connected with variation in pubescence. Figures 5 to 8 illustrate the four different situations we might possibly meet.

We may find, as in Fig. 5, that the light-colored flowers are all glabrous and that the dark-colored ones, though usually more or less pubescent, may occasionally be almost glabrous. These facts suggest, though they do not prove, that the light- and dark-colored plants are genetically isolated from each other, as when two well-isolated species are growing together. Again we may find, as in Fig. 6, that flower color and pubescence vary quite independently of one another. Another possibility is shown in Fig. 7; the two characters are completely correlated. The lightest-colored plants are the most glabrous, and the darkest are the most pubescent. The darker the color, the heavier the pubescence, without exception. Such a situation would result if color and pubescence were affected simultaneously by the same factor, as, for instance, moisture. The drier the site, shall we say, the lighter the color and the less developed the pubescence. With such a relationship a slight increase in color will always be accompanied by a slight increase in hairiness.

In Fig. 8 is represented the kind of result that is caused by introgression. In such a population color intensity and pubescence *tend* to go together but the relation is not absolute. Numerous pairs of individuals could be picked out in which one is very much darker than the other, but no more pubescent or perhaps even a little less so. Similarly one could select pairs in which the more pubescent plant was no darker or possibly even a little lighter. For the population as a whole, however, there is a very clear tendency for the darker plants to be the hairier, for the hairier to be the darker. It is also clear that on the whole the lighter plants are more glabrous and the most glabrous plants are lighter colored.

If both characters, as in this hypothetical illustration, are multifactorial, the only possible explanation for such a population is introgression. Darkness is due to many genes; heavy pubescence is due to many genes. On the whole these two sets of genes tend to occur together. If, as in Fig. 6, darkness and pubescence were both highly variable but were not correlated, then we could explain the high variability as due to any one of several causes that make for genic variability (high mutation rates, population pattern, etc.). If, however, they are both variable and both multigenic, then we would have to assume that gene changes affecting pubescence tended to be accompanied by gene changes affecting color intensity. No such kind of multidirection mutation is known.

If species differed only by two such characters as these, the ability to prove introgression from population analysis alone, though it would rest on a sound theoretical basis, would be too tenuous to be convincing. Species, however, differ in a large number of ways. In the population examples of Iris diagrammed in detail in Chapter 6 there was an association between redness of corolla and size of sepal which indicated introgression. In these same populations, how-

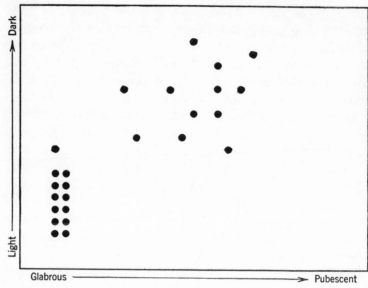

FIG. 5

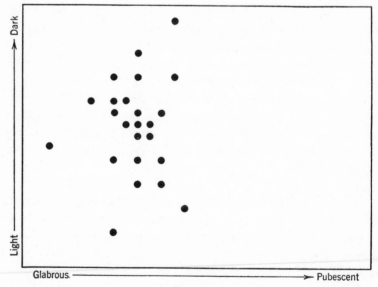

FIG. 6

FIGS. 5, 6, 7, and 8. Four possible kinds of relationship between two figure represents a hypothetical sample of 25 individuals, each one scored indication of introgression.

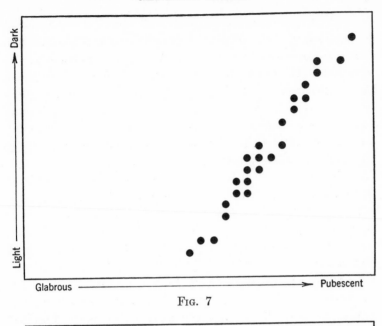

FIG. 7

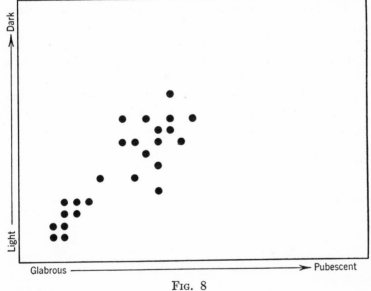

FIG. 8

different characters such as leaf pubescence and flower color. Each
for flower color and degree of pubescence. Only in Fig. 8 is there any
Further explanation in the text.

ever, there was also conspicuous and measurable variation in exsertion of the stamens, in the color pattern of the sepal, and in the size and proportion of the stylar appendages. As is shown in the diagrams that accompany Chapter 6, it can be demonstrated that all these characters tend to be somewhat correlated with redness of corolla and size of sepal. Scores, if not hundreds, of genes are involved. The only known mechanism that would explain their tendency to go together (which is far from absolute) is their having been introduced together into the population. These complexes of characters, which are statistically demonstrable, are the visible results of linkage systems and of other cohesive forces.

When, by the methods outlined in Chapter 6, one can work over the facts of correlation tendencies in these introgressed populations and produce exact, technical descriptions of the introgressing species, even when it is unknown to the observer, the proof of the underlying assumptions is as absolute as one might ever hope for in scientific work. The methods are still crude; it takes experience to use them effectively; but they have already advanced to the stage where they can be given to a group of graduate students as a class exercise. Such a group of students, given representative mass collections (Anderson, 1941) of a hybrid population, can reasonably be expected to draw up a technical description of the original hybridizing entities that produced the population.

CHAPTER 4

Introgression in Finite
Populations

Up to this point our discussion has considered the effects of linkage in restricting the kinds of recombinations that can occur in a species cross. Linkage also restricts their frequencies, a fact that becomes important when we proceed to discuss the probable fates of hybrid generations beyond the F_2. Since the individuals of the first hybrid generation are essentially similar genetically, it made very little difference in considering the recombinations achievable in the F_2 whether we were considering populations of scores, or of hundreds, or of thousands. Any two or three F_1 plants if crossed together will give essentially the same F_2 as will any two or three others. With the F_3 this is all changed. In a species cross the number of genetically different F_2 individuals certainly runs into the hundreds and might well be in the thousands. Therefore, in any finite F_2 population, most of the plants will be genetically distinct, and there may be great differences between different F_3 populations. In considering what would happen in the F_3, we must not only calculate the F_2 types that *might* occur and become the parents of the F_3; we must also consider which are *most likely* to occur.

To facilitate the discussion of these matters, let us construct a hypothetical case of linkage between 2 multiple-factor characters, leaf pubescence and leaf shape. Let us suppose that there are 2 pairs of genes, A vs. a and C vs. c, which have simple additive effects on leaf shape, so that $AACC$ is broad at the apex, while $aacc$ is narrow at the apex and broad at the base, and $AaCc$ is exactly intermediate. In the same way we shall imagine genes B vs. b and D vs. d affecting pubescence so that $BBDD$ is strongly pubescent, *bbdd* is completely glabrous, and *BbDd* is exactly intermediate.

What we shall now consider is the way in which the cross between a strongly obovate, heavily pubescent *AABBCCDD*

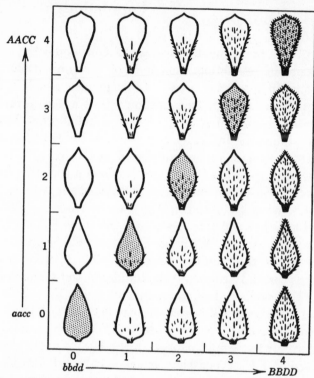

Fig. 9. A hypothetical example of multiple factor differences affecting two characters, leaf shape and pubescence. Genes *B* and *D* vs. *b* and *d* are supposed to have equal effects upon pubescence and none upon leaf shape. Genes *A* and *C* vs. *a* and *c* are supposed to have equal effects upon leaf shape and none upon pubescence. The frequencies of Figs. 10 to 17 all refer to this figure. The predominating leaf types in the "spindle of recombination" are slightly darker than the other types.

and a strongly ovate, completely glabrous *aabbccdd* will be affected by linkage. We are assuming that there is no dominance and no complicated gene interactions and that all 4 genes affecting each character have simple, additive effects. Were there no linkage all possible recombinations of these 2 characters would be achieved in an F_2 of reasonable size. The 16 recombination types illustrated in Fig. 9 would, in a population of 256, be expected with the frequencies shown in Fig. 10. In other words, there would be a great many intermediate leaves more or less like the F_1 ($AaBbCcDd$), and the 4 extreme recombinations ($AABB$-$CCDD$, $aaBBccDD$, $AAbbCCdd$, and $aabbccdd$) would be

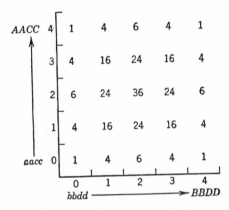

Fig. 10. Frequencies of the leaf types shown in Fig. 9, to be expected in an F_2 of 256 plants between an ovate-glabrous parent (0, 0) and an obovate-pubescent parent (4, 4) if there were no linkage.

rare. All 4 of these corner extremes are equally likely to appear, and all 4 are true breeding, whereas the percentage of homozygosity is lowest in the center of the chart. There would, therefore, be a tendency in later generations for these extreme types to be more frequent, the exact results depending on the natural mating system, the size of the populations, etc.

If, however, genes A, B, C, D, were linked (and in that order) and were close enough together so that double crossovers were either never produced or produced with such a low frequency that for statistical purposes they could be disregarded, then all the possible types of the F_2 are diagrammed in Fig. 11, along with their expected frequencies in a population of 144. It will be seen that the population would be made up largely of the recombinations along a diagonal spindle through the figure (the "recombination spindle" of Chapter 3). Nothing like the recombinations of the upper left-hand corner or the lower right-hand corner could appear. In other words, pubescence would tend

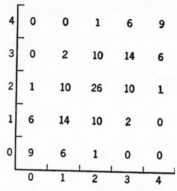

	0	1	2	3	4
4	0	0	1	6	9
3	0	2	10	14	6
2	1	10	26	10	1
1	6	14	10	2	0
0	9	6	1	0	0

	0	1	2	3	4
4	0	0	1	12	36
3	0	2	28	98	12
2	1	28	140	28	1
1	12	98	28	2	0
0	36	12	1	0	0

FIG. 11. Frequencies from the same cross as Fig. 10 if the genes A, B, C, and D were linked and in that order and if there were regularly one crossover, but no more. Expectations in an F_2 of 144 plants if crossovers were equally frequent at any point.

FIG. 12. The effect of localized chiasmata upon the frequencies of Fig. 11. Expectations in an F_2 of 576 plants if crossing over between B and C were four times as likely as between A and B or C and D.

strongly to be correlated with leaf shape; hairy-obovate and glabrous-ovate types would be common, in addition to intermediates like the F_1. Approaches to the extreme recombinations would be in the minority. Take, for instance, the types of leaves which are intermediate between the F_1 (2/2) and the two extreme recombination corners 5/0 and 0/5. They fall at 4/2 and 2/4 on Fig. 9. The first is a fairly obovate leaf with scattered pubescence, the latter a distinctly ovate leaf with quite heavy pubescence. Though theoretically, individuals of these two types could occur, either of them would be expected only once in 72 times, whereas leaves resembling the F_1 (2/2) would be 13 times as frequent and would be expected 26 in 144 times, making up nearly one fifth of the population. This is on the hypothesis that there is no localization of chiasmata, in other words, that crossing over between a and B is as likely to occur as between B and C and that either of these is as likely as crossing over between C and D. With such localization the restriction upon frequencies would be even greater. Figure 12 shows the expectations in a population of 576, if crossing over between B and C were 4 times as likely to occur as between A and B or C and D.

In other words, if we consider the "recombination spindle" connecting the two extreme parental types, the effect of linkage upon frequencies is to restrict the actual F_2 individuals in any finite population to a spindle. Any tendency toward localization of chiasmata will restrict this inner spindle still further, the force of the restriction depending on the degree of localization.

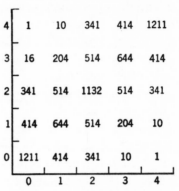

FIG. 13. The drift in future generations. Expectations for an F_3 of 10,368 plants if all the plants of Fig. 11 had been self-pollinated and each had contributed 72 seedlings to the next generation.

What kind of an F_3 can be expected from this finite F_2? The exact answer will depend on the mating system, the population size, etc. Let us take as an illustration a relatively large population with no differential viability and calculate the expectations if all the recombinations of Fig. 11 had actually occurred and each had contributed, by self-pollination, 72 plants to the next generation. The results are shown in Fig. 13. It will be seen that recombinations outside the "recombination spindle" of the F_2, though theoretically possible, are in a small minority. For plants approaching the glabrous-obovate or ovate-hairy, there are only 42 in 10,368 which are more extreme recombinations than any of those in the F_2.

Up to this point we have considered merely the effect of linkage in any one chromosome. Actually, of course, the recombination of any 2 multiple-factor characters will depend on how many genes are concerned, how they are distributed through the chromosomes, and the chromosome number. As an instructive limiting case, let us consider the recombinations of 2 multiple-factor characters, each due to a large number of genes more or less evenly distributed between the chromosomes. Let us suppose that there was only 1 pair of chromosomes and complete linkage. In the F_2 we would have only 3 types of individuals—those with both chromosomes from one parent, those with 1 of each, and those with both of the other. Our recombination spindle would be a line reaching from one parental corner to the other with frequencies of 1 at each end and of 2 in the middle. With 2 pairs of chromosomes and with the other conditions remaining the same, we have 5 possible types of F_2 individuals, with frequencies of 1–4–6–4–1. Again, as a recombination spindle, they would be restricted to an absolute line running from one corner of our figure, to the F' position in the center, to the opposite diagonal corner.

With more and more chromosomes, as long as the genes for the 2 characters were many and were distributed at random, we would still have an absolutely attentuated recombination spindle consisting of a mere diagonal line across the square representing all the possible recombinations. The larger the number of chromosomes, the greater would be the chance of achieving F_2 recombinations very similar to the F_1, and the slighter would be that of recombinations similar to one parent or the other. With a large number of chromosomes there might be many possible genotypes, but they would all go in a graded series from one parental extreme, to the F_1, to the other parental extreme, and increase in one character in the direction of one of the parents would always be accompanied by a corresponding increase in the same direction by the other character.

If the genes affecting multiple-factor characters, however, were not distributed at random between the chromosomes a much wider recombination spindle would be possible. If such genes were entirely on separate chromosomes for each character we might hope to achieve a random sample of the entire recombination square. Suppose, for instance, that the leaf shape and pubescence of the previous example had each been due to many genes, that substantially all the genes for pubescence were in 3 chromosomes, and that substantially all those for leaf shape were in any other 3, then our recombination spindle would expand to fill the entire recombination square, and all the recombination types of Fig. 9 might be achieved if we raised enough hybrids. There is as yet no published evidence showing that multiple factors can be distributed in any such way, however, and it is generally believed among geneticists that the genes affecting any one character are distributed pretty much at random. So much for the hypothetical limiting case of all-linked. As has been pointed out above the amounts of crossing over which we do actually obtain are not very far, comparatively speaking, from this actual limit. In each chromosome we shall have the restrictive effects shown in Fig. 10. For the chromosomes as a whole we shall have recombinations restricted closely to the axis of the recombination spindle, except as nonrandom distribution of multiple-factor genes between chromosomes allows more extreme combinations. The resultant of these combined effects will be the same kind of narrow recombination spindle running through the center of all imaginable recombinations. Linkage, in other words, takes what would have been a spherical mass of probabilities and draws them out towards the original parental positions. We may think of linkage in two ways, either as a negative force that keeps new recombinations from appearing, or as a strong positive force tending to bring the hybrid population back to something very like the original types. While it operates in both of these ways, its positive pull back to the original recombination is stronger. *It is, therefore, more effective to think of linkage as a factor of racial and specific cohesion rather than as a barrier between species and between races.*

The continuing effect of linkage, generation after generation, is suggested in Fig. 13. With self-pollination there is a strong tendency to return to the original parental combinations of characters. Within the recombination spindle, there is in the F_2 zero heterozygosity at either end, rising to 50 per cent in the middle. Therefore, recombinations like the original parents tend to reproduce themselves, whereas intermediate ones segregate. Were there no linkage this segregation would radiate equally in all four directions from each heterozygote. Linkage causes the segregation to be much greater in the direction of the recombination spindle. Figures 14 to 17 show the populations to be expected upon self-fertilization of certain F_2 types. In each case, it will be noted, the recombinations of the F_3 are oriented in the general direction of the F_2 recombination spindle and, like it, have their greatest frequencies along the center of the spindle. The combined effects of (a) restriction to the recombination spindle and (b) the comparative heterozygosity of forms resembling the F_1 would be to increase in subsequent generations the proportions of individuals rather similar to, or identical with, the original parents. Backcrossing would, of course, greatly accelerate this tendency. Although these calculations are based upon what would happen with self-fertilization, all other forms of inbreeding would cause the same general result but at a slower rate. With continuous cross-pollination, in small populations, for instance, the inbreeding caused by the population size would eventually have the same effect.

We therefore conclude that the cohesive force of linkage would be more apparent in the F_3 and succeeding generations than they had been in the F_2. The restriction upon types of recombinations would persist and would be joined by the effect of linkage upon frequencies. The combination of these influences renders unlikely the possibility that the recombinations of the F_3 and subsequent generations could advance very much outside the recombination of the F_2.

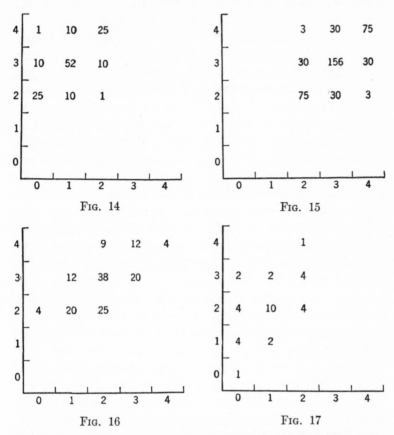

Figs. 14–17. Types and frequencies expected in the F_3 from self-pollinating four of the F_2 plants of Fig. 11. Note that in the F_3 the frequencies of each selfing still tend to align themselves in accord with the "recombination spindle" of the F_2. The scale is that of Fig. 9.

Although this conclusion is based on theory, it is in accord with practical experience. In such endeavors as attempting to recombine the desirable qualities of two inbred lines of maize, it is one of the problems of modern corn breeding that

recombinations resembling either parental inbred are easy
to achieve, whereas recombinations of one quality to a degree
resembling one parent and of another quality to a degree
resembling the other parent are difficult, if not impossible.

However, the question of just how strong the cohesive effects of linkage might be, were it the only barrier between
species or races, is an academic one. In most cases that have
so far been investigated there were other isolating mechanisms, all of them operating in the same general direction.
The selective effect of the habitat, discussed in detail in
Chapter 2, is almost universal in such crosses. Usually, it
will be remembered, it favors hybrids and backcrosses closely
resembling the parental species. In addition, there are such
barriers as geographic isolation, differences in blooming
season, differential pollen-tube growth, inversions of chromosome segments, chromosome interchanges, polyploidy, and
the like. Species are kept apart by barriers of various kinds,
both internal and external, working together in various ways.
Like linkage, many of these barriers continue to operate in
hybrid populations. Though they operate in different ways
and at different times in the life cycle, their overall effect is
the encouragement of gene recombinations like those of the
parental species at the expense of more radical rearrange-
ments.

It has been found that species which are completely interfertile in the experimental plot often yield no hybrids unless
artificially cross-pollinated. Anderson and Schafer (1931),
for instance, found that, though Aquilegia plants were out-
crossed within the species, no hybrid seed were produced
when several plants of various species were grown side by
side. Mather (1947) has begun the exact analysis of such a
situation in Antirrhinum. He finds the barrier to reside in
the flower-visiting habits of the insects responsible for cross-
fertilization. A delicately adjusted barrier of this sort would
restrict gene flow to particular times and places, rendering
the two species effectively shut off from each other most of
the time, yet allowing introgression frequently enough to

have an effect upon population dynamics. The overall result of these various external and internal barriers seems to be exactly that. It permits a surprising amount of gene flow between well-differentiated species and races, without on the other hand allowing these species and races to lose their identity.

Among the forces producing species and races, linkage is of particular importance because of its complete universality. It results from the fact that all germplasms are made up of long chainlike proteins. It is, therefore, an always present force. When by any process, accidental or otherwise, the gene differences between two strains become 3 or more in any chromosome region that ordinarily has no more than 1 chiasma, it begins to operate. *Linkage may, therefore, provide the necessary initial isolation that allows other internal isolating mechanisms to accumulate under the action of natural selection.*

As an example of the way in which linkage might take the lead in building up specific or racial isolation, let us return to our hypothetical leaf shapes and pubescences in Fig. 9, where there are 4 linked genes. Had these differences arisen gradually in a large population, with active cross-breeding, they might have been distributed independently of each other in the population so that all the combinations of leaf shape and pubescence illustrated in Fig. 9 could have been represented. Suppose that in some way the population was decimated and that the only survivors happened to be the extreme ovate-glabrous type of the lower left-hand corner (0/0) and the extreme pubescent-obovate one of the upper right (4/4). Linkage alone would be a strong enough force so that if these two strains came together again it would be difficult, even with strong artificial selection, to reconstitute all the eliminated types. Exactly what would happen would depend upon the relative numbers of the two surviving strains, and the breeding structure of the population. Without extremely strong selection away from such a condition they would tend to make a population with 2 centers of variability instead of the original 1. There would be a hairy-obovate strain and an ovate-glabrous one. Though intermediates could be produced and variation might be great in some populations, the chances of ever again attaining the random frequencies of the original population would be extremely small. Even strong artificial selection could scarcely recreate the extreme leaf types 4/0 and 0/4. The population would now have 2 centers of variation; it would have acquired the necessary minimum differentiation upon which further isolating mechanisms could accumulate.

CHAPTER 5

Introgression and Evolution

It is premature to attempt any generalizations as to the importance of introgressive hybridization in evolution. There is some evidence, mostly inferential, that it did indeed play a role. There are as yet no critical data to indicate whether that role was a major or minor one. Though it is certainly true that one cannot state with assurance that introgression was a major factor in evolution, it is quite as true that we cannot yet be certain that it was *not* a major factor. The chief purpose of this book is to indicate the kind of critical data that are needed before such questions as this can be discussed intelligently.

One problem that cannot be settled satisfactorily without further information is the extent to which the term introgression can be validly used. In the original instance it described introgression of one species into another. In many ways the flow of genes from one subspecies into another, or from one variety into another, or from one genus into another presents the same phenomenon. In other ways there are distinct peculiarities at each of these levels. We shall have to be much more fully informed before we can intelligently set exact limits to the use of the term. Throughout this book an attempt has been made to discuss the phenomenon on so fundamental a level that the term introgression would apply with equal validity whether the entities involved were subspecies, species, or genera.

If introgression proves to be a primary factor in evolution it will be because it so greatly enriches variation in the participating species. As raw material for evolution, the bizarre hybrid swarms described in Chapter 1 are not so important as the Asclepias introgression described by Woodson (1947), which was barely noticeable in any one locality and extended as a trend through a long intermediate zone. By the time of the third backcross of the original hybrid to one of the parental species, there would be little or no external indication of hybridity in the mongrel progeny. Yet in terms of gene frequencies, the effects of introgression in such mongrels would far outweigh the immediate effects of gene mutation.

Such otherwise excellent studies of hybridization under natural conditions as those of Epling (1947) on Salvia, and those of Valentine (1948) on Primula, fall short of their greatest possible usefulness because they present neither precise data nor even rough estimates on this important point. Having in each case demonstrated that hybridization occurs frequently in nature, that the hybrids are partially fertile, and that some backcrossing does occur, they rest their case. Impressed by the evident fact that hybridization is not occurring on a scale large enough to have taxonomic consequences, they do not inquire into the more biologically significant problem *whether it is having genetic consequences.* A trickle of genes so slight as to be without any practical taxonomic result might still be many times more important than mutation in keeping up the basic variability of the parental species. The critical question, on which we have as yet almost no data, but which it should eventually be possible to answer exactly, is "How much of the variation in the supposedly pure parental populations is due to introgression?" There are some circumstantial data suggesting that introgression may be one of the main sources of that variability which provides the raw material for evolution. Woodson's detailed studies of *Asclepias tuberosa* and Turrill's and Marsden-Jones' work on Silene (see Marsden-Jones and Turrill, 1946) are examples of the kind of data we shall need before we can even discuss such a problem.

Nearly all the published data on introgression demonstrate its importance in areas where man has upset natural forces. We might logically expect that introgression would be equally effective when nature herself does the upsetting. Floods, fires, tornadoes, and hurricanes must certainly have operated upon natural vegetation long before the advent of man.

Like man himself all these phenomena alter conditions catastrophically, break down barriers between species, and provide unusual new habitats in which hybrid derivatives may for a time find a foothold, thus serving as a bridge by which groups of genes from one species can invade the germ-plasm of another.

Not until one has lived in close proximity to a large mid-continental river does he realize what a restless neighbor such a waterway can be. It is forever changing its course and altering the habitats of plants that grow near it. Trees are undermined and swept away; sand to the depth of several feet is deposited on top of heavy clays or silt, thus changing the soil type and the ground-water level; plants are transported bodily; and not only do water levels change from day to day and week to week, but also the average level of the previous decade may be drastically altered by a whim of the river. In such a variable environment species that (through introgression) are able to achieve a great increase in genic variability should be at a selective advantage. It is apparently true that river-valley plants are more generally adaptable than those from other habitats. It would seem likely that introgression may be one of the natural forces that have brought about this greater adaptability. Exact data bearing on this point should not be difficult to obtain.

A demonstration of the evolutionary importance of "natural" introgression on a much wider scale is emerging from a series of studies by various workers which are already well under way but for the most part have not yet been formally published. All suggest the probable importance of introgression at particular times and places when diverse floras were brought together in a changing environment. Mason and his collaborators (1942; see also Cain, 1944), working with living and fossil populations of the closed cone pines, are finding it possible to demonstrate these phenomena in a surprisingly exact fashion. Areas that were once a series of islands off the California coast have been united to the mainland by natural causes. In these areas species of pines that were previously isolated have been brought together in a newly emerged area in which somewhat diverse floras were in the process of settling down into a new, and supposedly more stable, equilibrium. Hybridization and introgression under such conditions might be able to play a much greater role than in a stabilized community of which all the members have long been selected for their ability to interlock effectively.

Woodson (1947) has presented data on the introgression between three well-differentiated geographical races of *Asclepias tuberosa* (butterfly weed). One of these is centered upon peninsular Florida, a region that was an island, or series of islands, in Tertiary times and was later connected with the mainland. Through introgression, the fusion of these two varieties has now become a gradual process, extending over an intermediate zone hundreds of miles in depth. The infiltration of the two varieties is so gradual as to be imperceptible to anything less acute than refined statistical methods. From what is generally known about the flora of northern Florida and the Gulf and Atlantic coastal plains it seems probable that the introgression of these two varieties of Asclepias is rather typical of that area. For genus after genus in the flora of the eastern states, there are well-differentiated species or varieties in southern and central Florida and equally well-differentiated entities on the Coastal Plain. In northern Florida there is centered an intermediate zone in which various transitions between the typical coastal-plain type and the typical peninsular type make up the bulk of the populations. It would seem as if, when "Orange Island" was united to the mainland for the last time, two rather differentiated floras may have met in this intermediate zone. Under these unusual conditions, not only would there have been special opportunities for hybridization, but also, with two sets of plants readjusting themselves into new communities, some of the backcrosses would have been at a selective advantage. Thus introgression would have been encouraged in much the same ways as when man upsets the ordinary balance of nature.

It is probable that the same kind of phenomenon took place in the eastern United States after the last glaciation. Whenever the retreat of the continental ice was rapid, large areas must have been open for colonization, and sometimes at least they must have presented the invaders with new sets of soil types and habitats different from those previously known. When the ice front advanced again it may very likely have left isolated pockets of vegetation well behind the readvancing front. If these areas were small, the "Sewall Wright effect" would have produced local differentiation within the pocket so that at the next time of retreat there would be opportunities for these new highly localized varieties to introgress into the main body of the species. The distribution and differentiation of the northern blue flags (*Iris versicolor* and *Iris virginica*) suggest that a considerable area in the interior of the lower peninsula of Michigan may have been isolated for quite a time in this fashion. W. H. Camp has already given an informal report (1943) on his studies of hybridization in North American beeches (Fagus) which demonstrate the effect of the various retreats and advances of the ice front on introgression in that genus. With a series of studies on different genera we should be able to approach the subject experimentally rather than dogmatically.

It seems probable that a somewhat similar mass introgression may have taken place in the northern and eastern Ozarks in post-glacial times. During the xerothermic period when the prairie grasslands extended much farther east than they do now, many of our common woodland species of eastern North America must have existed in the Ozarks in small, isolated refuges. Today, in much the same way, small patches of isolated woodland are to be found in sheltered canyons in western Oklahoma. When the climate was distinctly hotter and drier than it is now, the central Ozarks in southern Missouri must have had a climate more like that of western Oklahoma today. With an increasingly severe climate and with small populations, opportunities for differentiation would have been great. As the hot, dry period came to a close and the mesophytic forests moved westward again, these remnants probably first spread out locally and then hybridized with their remote cousins as they came back into the territory. Desmarais (1947) has made an intensive study of the sugar maples which demonstrates something of what took place in that genus. More than one observant naturalist has noted slight regional differences in the Ozark representatives of many other wide-ranging species, which would indicate that the phenomenon may have been a very general one.

In his studies of introgression in Cistus (1941) Dansereau presented circumstantial evidence that the North African variety of *C. ladaniferus* originated through introgression of *C. laurifolius* into the typical variety (which is now limited to the Iberian peninsula and southern France). Although he presented no cytological or genetical evidence in support of this hypothesis, he did possess a detailed understanding of the genus Cistus from having monographed it and from having, as a trained ecologist, studied the problem in the field. Furthermore, he made detailed population samples that were analyzed by some of the methods discussed in Chapter 6. His explanation seems to be well established as a working hypothesis. If confirmed, it would be a further demonstration of the role of introgression in differentiating geographical varieties.

INTROGRESSION AND EVOLUTION UNDER DOMESTICATION

Such disturbances of the habitat as those previously described certainly must have occurred in prehuman times. It is just as certain that the appearance of man greatly accelerated such processes. On the one hand, by moving himself and his domesticated animals from place to place he removed geographical barriers between previously isolated species. On the other, he created new ecological niches in which hybrid segregates might find a foothold. Some of these niches were of definite types, and he created them everywhere he went. Of these one of the most important was his trash and dung heaps. He made these everywhere he halted, and, as he unconsciously bred the quick-growing weeds capable of utilizing soils high in nitrogen, he also unconsciously carried them about from place to place and gave them previously unparalleled opportunities to cross with others of their kind and thus build up into superweeds. From these weeds some of his crops were bred. There is good evidence that hemp started in that way, and from what was originally a weed plant there were at length evolved hemp as a fiber plant, hemp as a source of oil (from the seeds), and hemp as a narcotic drug (Vavilov, 1926; Parodi, 1935). The primitive chenopodiums and amaranths which are so widely grown as cereals by primitive peoples, in both the old world and new, show every indication of having originated in this fashion. Many of the cucurbits probably originated in the same way. Most, if not all, of the wild cucurbits are bitter or insipid. Introgression produced weed types that became camp followers. These were probably used first as dishes or rattles. Increasing variation produced some whose seeds were edible, and, still later, varieties with edible flesh were selected.

Evolution under domestication has been so complete that it is difficult to get exact data on the subject. In only a few instances can we point to the exact wild species from which a cultivated plant or a weed was derived. For some of the cultivated plants we know closely related wild species, though we have little or no evidence of the exact relation between them and the cultivated plant. In many other cases we can point to a group of weeds that are related to a cultivated plant. This is no solution to the problem. We now know that weeds may be bred from cultivated plants, as well as vice versa. Since weeds as we know them are largely man-made and inhabit ecological niches that are either directly or indirectly the results of man's interference, our "explanation" of the origin of such a crop is merely the posing of a much larger problem. Where and how were the cultivated plant and its related weeds bred out of the pre-human elements in the genus? Most of our cultivated plants, therefore, merely tell us that evolution has proceeded apace under domestication. Few of them are the kind of research material from which we can get a precise answer as to how the changes that occurred under domestication were brought about.

Accordingly, we shall first present (in simplified, pictorialized form) a hypothetical, generalized diagram of the way in which domestication of weeds and cultivated plants most probably took place. With that for reference, there will then be presented detailed evidence from various genera supporting the hypothesis. Plate 3, therefore, is a diagram of the way in which cultivated plants and weeds have been consciously and unconsciously developed from their wild progenitors. *It is greatly simplified as compared with the actual history of most cultivated plants and weeds.* For one thing, the special and complicating effects of polyploidy and apomixis are not included. With the occurrence of apomixis or of ploidy either before or after domestication, further complications would be added to the existing complexities of relationship.

Turning to Plate 3, the diagram at the top of the plate concerns the five original entities in our mythical genus Planta and their fate under the influence of man. The diagram represents an area of continental size with one highly localized species, "*P. endemica*," in the east, and another species, "*P. occidentale*," in the far west. In the center of the continent are three entities, "*P. laxa*" and the two entities that we have grouped under "*P. mixta*," the variety "*cruciformis*" and the variety "*punctata*." *Planta cruciformis* and *P. punctata* are fairly well differentiated and for the most part occupy different areas, but in the zone where they approach each other (even in prehuman times) there was some hy-

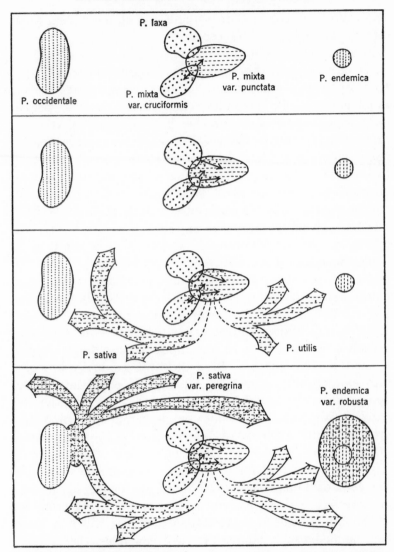

PLATE 3. Introgression under the influence of man. Diagram showing the role of introgression in building up cultivated plants and weeds in the hypothetical genus Planta. The ranges of the various species and varieties are represented upon an area of supposedly continental size. The plate shows the ranges of the species and varieties in prehuman times (at the top), then the successive steps by which the present condition (bottom of the plate) has been brought about. Further discussion in the text.

bridization and consequent introgression of genes from each into the germplasm of the other.

The second part of the diagram shows the unconscious effect of man upon this assemblage. When he occupies the territory, even though at first he takes no particular interest in the genus Planta, he removes barriers between the species and creates new ecological niches in which some of the hybrid segregates might survive. Consequently there is greatly increased introgression of *P. cruciformis* into *P. punctata* (we visualize *cruciformis* as being a weedy, rank, quick-growing, many-seeded plant even under natural conditions and likely, therefore, to contribute genes that would be at a selective advantage after the appearance of man). In addition, the barriers between *P. laxa* and *P. mixta* are broken down enough so that we get introgression of *laxa* into *P. mixta* var. *punctata*. Since *laxa* and *punctata* are highly differentiated species, the introduction of a relatively few genes will produce an increase in overall variability.

As this reciprocal introgression continues, it produces certain new recombinations that are outstandingly useful to man, and at length some of these are gradually brought into cultivation. A new crop plant has come into being which we shall call *P. utilis*. Similarly, the addition of *cruciformis* genes to this same complex produces a more aggressive plant that grows of its own accord in the fields where *utilis* is being cultivated. Eventually, under the combined effects of natural selection, conscious human selection, and unconscious human selection, there are produced an aggressive weed, *P. sativa*, and an important world crop, *P. utilis*, both of which are spread more and more widely as they become increasingly adapted to their new roles.

After many years *P. utilis* is cultivated within the narrow area to which *P. endemica* has been so long restricted. Eventually an occasional hybrid is produced which backcrosses into the original *P. endemica*. The introduction of a very few genes from *P. utilis* greatly increases the variability and adaptability of *P. endemica*. As a result, though only slightly changed morphologically, it is now able to colonize a much larger territory than that to which it had previously been restricted, and it does, in fact, become almost "weedy" in its habits.

Meanwhile, by other routes, man has unwittingly carried his new weed *P. sativa* into the area of *P. occidentalis*. There the two hybridize and the hybrids backcross to *P. sativa*, increasing its variability still more. From the resulting intermixture there is bred a new and particularly aggressive form of this weed which spreads around the world and eventually becomes recognized as *P. sativa* var. *peregrina*.

So much for a part of the history of domestication in the hypothetical genus Planta. Let us now consider the difficulties of unraveling this history had Planta been an actual genus. We would have had little or no evidence about it as it occurred in prehuman or even in early human times. From the bewildering array of specimens in our herbaria, collected by different people and in a more or less haphazard fashion, from notes by agronomists who had cultivated *P. utilis*, and from our own powers of observation we should have had to put the story together. This would have been difficult. Someone interested in *P. sativa* might never have been able to make field studies in the original region where introgression took place so actively in *P. mixta*. Only occasionally would careful local field studies reveal to the scientific world such interesting phenomena as the effect of *P. utilis* on *P. endemica*. Were the work to be done by purely conventional taxonomic methods, based upon the critical study and comparison of single specimens, a first-rate taxonomist might separate the genus into the following categories: (1) *endemica*, (2) *mixta*, (3) *utilis-sativa*, and (4) *occidentale*. From collections of single individuals it would not be possible to distinguish between the original *endemica* and its variety *robusta*. One could not in every instance separate some variants of *sativa* from some of those of *utilis*. *Planta sativa peregrina* could not be differentiated from *sativa*, and the intergrades between *punctata* and *cruciformis* would be con-

fused with *sativa* and with *utilis*. Had population samples
of these entities been examined, however, it would have been

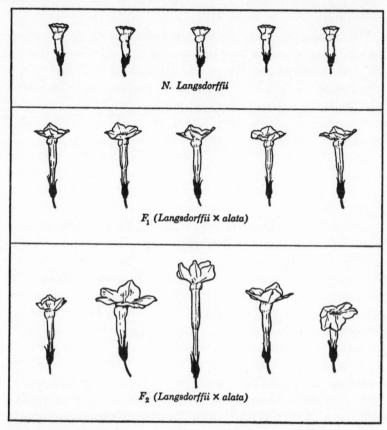

N. *Langsdorffii*

F_1 (*Langsdorffii* × *alata*)

F_2 (*Langsdorffii* × *alata*)

PLATES 4 and 5.   The basic facts of the genetics of species crosses, graphically summarized.   Shown to scale are representative flowers of *Nicotiana Langsdorffii*, *N. alata*, their F_1 and F_2 hybrids, and backcrosses of
the F_1 to each parent species.   Note the uniform and intermediate F_1,
the highly variable F_2, and the generally close resemblance of each backcross to its recurrent parent.

possible to define these entities exactly and to distinguish
between them.   Furthermore, by such methods as those
outlined in Chapter 6 one could have considered the dynamics of the whole group.   He could have demonstrated

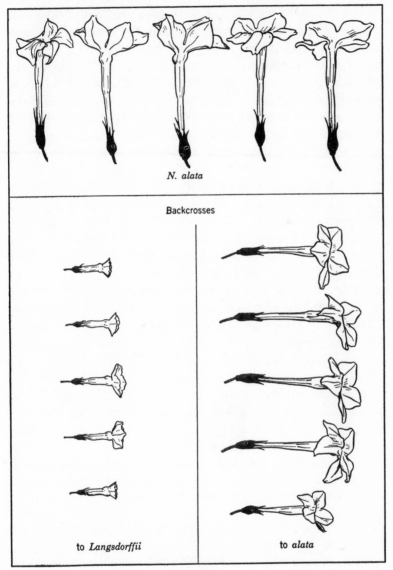

N. alata

Backcrosses

to *Langsdorffii*   to *alata*

PLATE 5

that *sativa peregrina* differed from *sativa* by genes acquired from *P. occidentalis* and shown how a slight introgression from *utilis* had produced *P. endemica* var. *robusta*.

For the great bulk of our cultivated plants it will be difficult, or impossible, to bring together the data on wild populations, weed populations, and geographical distribution which will permit us to demonstrate step by step these complicated processes of domestication. The major areas of domestication (Asia Minor, Southeastern Asia) are difficult of access to most students. However, there are a few cultivated plants and weeds whose histories are more accessible, and for a few of them data on introgression are already beginning to appear. Of these the common cultivated sunflower, *Helianthus annuus*, is in a class by itself in the degree to which we may some day hope to demonstrate in detail the steps by which it became a cultivated plant and a weed. It was domesticated in pre-Columbian times within the boundaries of the present United States. A considerable amount of prehistoric remains from archaeological sites are already available in museums. Its wild progenitors are still to be found in the United States in the west, south, and southwest. Heiser has already (1947*a*, 1947*b*, 1949) made a promising beginning at unraveling the story of its domestication. Though, in comparison with the great world crops such as rice, wheat, and maize, the history of the sunflower is a relatively simple one, it is so complicated that a decade or so of intensive work will be needed to establish the main points. As the story takes shape with such data as are now available, it is about as follows:

If we use the expression *Helianthus annuus* in its widest sense, there can at present be recognized the following different entities:

A. Cultivated large-headed varieties (chiefly monocephalic), grown for their large, oily seeds.

B. Large-headed and small-headed varieties grown for ornament.

C. Weeds of the Great Plains and adjacent prairies, oftentimes growing in corn fields, gardens, etc.

D. A second set of weeds, distinct from the preceding, limited to trash heaps, railroad yards, and the like, typical "camp followers."

E. A third set of weeds in the irrigated valleys of the far west.

It is already known from careful experimental work that the large-headed condition is due to a single recessive gene, whose exact expression is conditioned by a few modifying factors. It suppresses the production of axillary buds and therefore forces the maximum amount of growth into the single head, which consequently bears much larger seeds. We do not yet know from archaeological evidence just where this mutation was picked up. We do know that it occurred very early, possibly before the Christian era. Sauer (1936) has suggested that the sunflower was domesticated before maize reached North America. Certainly, by early Basket-Maker times in the southwest, the large-flowered sunflower was being grown; we have not only the large seeds as evidence but also some prehistoric collections of the heads themselves.

The large-headed sunflowers, both in prehistoric times and at the present day, were a diverse lot, including purple-seeded varieties with long, narrow seeds (still grown by the Hopi and in northern Mexico) and white- and gray-seeded varieties with shorter, flatter seeds. Morphologically all these varieties are closer to Weed D than they are to Weed C, suggesting either that the weed originated after the cultivated variety had been differentiated or that in some way or other the weed arose out of the same complex. Both A and D (the cultivated varieties and the camp-follower weed) show morphological relationships to more than one of the wild-growing species of category C. Heiser has already been able to demonstrate the introgression that is going on between the C variety of $H.$ $annuus$ and the very different $H.$ $petiolaris$ of the Great Plains. It seems very probable that A and C originated in early prehistoric times when the natural introgression between the various original entities in this group was accelerated by the presence of man. Out of the ensuing mixture came the cultivated plant and the camp-follower weed, the development of the former being very greatly accelerated by the appearance of the mutation of a large single head. Being recessive, single-headedness bred true as soon as its importance was realized, producing a superior crop that was more and more widely dispersed. In many areas to which it spread, it could by introgression contribute genes to the wild and weed sunflowers of the new area. Occasionally it might, through backcrossing, pick up a few useful genes from the wild sunflowers of that area. Ordinarily, however, the recessive nature of its most useful character (large-headedness) would have kept it from acquiring as many genes in this manner as it might otherwise have done.

Heiser's most complete evidence is for one of the later steps in this process. He has been able to demonstrate in detail the way in which one of the E categories has originated and is continuing to evolve. *Helianthus Bolanderi* was originally a distinctive, highly localized sunflower restricted to serpentine areas in northern California. Since the introduction of *Helianthus annuus* into that region, hybrids have occurred between the two species. Though they are very different from each other and the hybrids are partially sterile, enough introgression of *annuus* into *Bolanderi* has occurred to produce a vigorous weedy variant of the original serpentine sunflower. This more aggressive type is now spreading with increased rapidity in irrigated areas, continuing to cross occasionally with *H. annuus*, and is indeed a weed in the making. The main morphological facts are summarized in Table 3. Heiser analyzed the situation by field methods similar to those described in the next chapter and produced the above explanation as a working hypothesis. He then repeated the suspected cross between *Bolanderi* and *annuus*, grew progenies from suspected hybrids, and worked out the cytology of both species and their hybrids, both natural and artificial. His experimental data confirm and extend his original hypothesis, and the case has been proved beyond a reasonable doubt.

A similar demonstration of introgression between a cultivated plant and its weedy relative has been made by Marion Ownbey (unpublished). In the vicinity of Pullman,

Washington, a variety of garden lettuce (*Lactuca sativa*) with dark red leaves is widely grown. This color difference is dominant in crosses with weed lettuce (*Lactuca serriola*), and one can therefore recognize naturally occurring hybrids between the two lettuces. Ordinarily, because so many of the characteristics of cultivated lettuce are recessives accumulated under domestication, the hybrid looks so unlike garden

TABLE 3 *

Comparison of Morphological Features of *Helianthus annuus*,
H. Bolanderi, and Their Hybrid

	1	2	3	4
	H. Bolanderi (Serpentine, Foothill Race)	*H. Bolanderi* (Valley Weed Race)	*H. annuus* × *H. Bolanderi*	*H. annuus* (Western)
Height	3–10 dm.	6–13 dm.	6–15 dm.	8–18 dm.
Leaf Shape	Linear-lanceolate to ovate lanceolate, cuneate at base	Ovate-lanceolate to ovate, cuneate, rarely truncate at base	Ovate-lanceolate to ovate, cuneate to truncation at base	Ovate-lanceolate to ovate; truncate to cordate at base
Involucral Bracts	3.0–4.0 mm. broad; oblong to lanceolate, gradually attenuate	3.5–4.5 mm. broad; otherwise much as in 1	5.0–7.0 mm. broad; lanceolate to ovate; more abruptly attenuate than in 1 and 2, less so than in 4	5.0–7.0 mm. broad; lanceolate-ovate to ovate, abruptly attenuate
Pubescence	Hirsute or hirsute-villous	Hirsute, rarely somewhat hispid	Hirsute to hispid	Hispid
Ray Number	10–13	12–17	14–20	17–24
Diameter of Disk	1.5–2.0 cm.	2.0–2.5 cm.	2.0–3.0 cm.	2.5–3.5 cm.

* Adapted from Heiser (1947*b*).

lettuce that it escapes critical notice. Using the red-leaved character as a marker, Ownbey has been able to demonstrate the extensive introgression that is continually going on from garden lettuces into weed lettuces, previously largely unsuspected because the hybrids and hybrid derivative mongrels were superficially so similar to wild lettuce and so unlike garden lettuce.

An effective demonstration of the role of introgression in building up weed complexes is afforded by two species of fleabane, *Erigeron annuus* and *Erigeron strigosus* (= *E*.

ramosus). These two native American plants were originally quite distinct from one another and had very different ecological requirements. *Erigeron annuus* prefers rich, moist situations; *E. strigosus* is a plant of dry, barren areas. In the eastern United States they have introgressed so extensively into each other that somewhat intermediate types are found exclusively over wide areas. Apomictical forms of both *annuus* and *strigosus* have occurred, some of which seem to have been very widespread. Weed strains of both species have spread far outside their original habitats and have been carried to other continents.

In parts of their present ranges the two species have been so extensively blurred that it is difficult to conceive of what they may have been like before the advent of man. In other areas, however, they are well differentiated, though introgression is still continuing. Their relationships are quite clear in the northern Ozarks. There *Erigeron strigosus* forms large and only slightly variable populations in dry, rocky areas, while *Erigeron annuus*, in essentially pure condition, is limited to rich and fairly moist locations, such as barnyards and fertile vegetable gardens. Intermediate populations are common throughout the area, the degree of intermediacy being proportional to the dryness and sterility of the habitat. Yet this intermediacy is something inherent, since cultures raised in the experimental garden retain the characteristics of the populations from which they were derived.

With many cultivated plants the nature and degree of introgression have probably changed as man has found new uses for each cultivated plant. The probable histories of cucurbits and of hemp have already been alluded to. Seibert (1947, 1948) has discussed the role of introgression in the domestication of Para rubber (Hevea). The wild-growing species of Hevea are native mostly to alluvial soils, and Seibert thinks that there may have been some introgression in these areas before the advent of man. Apparently the species was first cultivated for its edible nuts (Baldwin, 1947; Baldwin and Schultes, 1947). Either accidentally or with intent, seedlings from wild trees came up in clearings where they were being used for food. These areas were often outside the natural range of that species or variety and sometimes within pollination distance of other species. Consequently these isolated trees tended to be cross-pollinated. Under the primitive agriculture of these areas, clearings were occupied for a time and then deserted. As the disturbed land gradually reverted to jungle there were many opportunities for the hybrid seedlings of the isolated nut trees to germinate and survive. They crossed back to the native species of that vicinity, and thus the process of introgression might have started in hundreds of little clearings in the jungle. The more or less casual use of Hevea for its edible nuts increased the natural introgression between some of the species. When man gradually learned that the latex of Hevea also had its applications, he already had at hand variable, introgressed, semidomesticated populations, in which trees superior in latex were more likely to be found.

The extent and frequency of introgression must certainly vary greatly with the type of agriculture that is being practiced. Under the jungle-clearing pattern, like that just described for Hevea, it must have been at a maximum. Today it can be seen to vary widely between areas of pastoral agriculture and those devoted exclusively to field crops. In the latter, in the so-called cotton belts, wheat belts, and corn belts, the native vegetation is completely removed over wide areas. Alien crop plants are introduced. There are few opportunities for hybridization and almost no niches in which the hybrid segregates may survive when they do occur. A pastured area is very different. The native vegetation is removed only in part, though natural ecological conditions are drastically changed. The plants introduced in pastures and hayfields are of many kinds. There are new opportunities for hybridization between various components of the native vegetation previously isolated, or between them and their close relatives among the introduced plants and weeds.

When hybrids do occur there are various new niches in which some of them may possibly succeed. It is significant that most of the studies of introgression up to the present time have been made in pastures or in heavily pastured areas. Riley's studies of Iris were made in pastured swamplands. Anderson and Hubricht worked in overpastured areas in the Ozarks. It would seem to be significant that New Zealand—where the frequency of hybridization has been the subject of several special investigations (Allan, 1937)—is very largely given over to pastoral agriculture. Such genera as Crataegus, in which thousands of new species have been described in the last century, are nearly all plants of pastures. For Crataegus, Marie Victorin has outlined the main steps in the production of the swarms of these new forms in the pastures of French Canada. The great majority of the species described by the late Charles S. Sargent came from such pastured areas in which opportunities for hybridization and consequent introgression were very high. Crataegus (a genus in which both polyploidy and apomixis are frequent) produced a complicated introgression pattern, which has led to great taxonomic confusion. Without these two complications there would have been a less ruffled gene flow between the original hybridizing entities.

The demonstration that cultivated plants and weeds are very largely the products of introgression is particularly important for plant genetics. It is almost exclusively upon such plants that the theory of plant genetics has been based. From Mendel's original peas to Blakeslee's Daturas, we have worked chiefly with introgressed germplasms. Some of our marker genes are certainly introgressive segments from another germplasm. That does not vitiate their use as marker genes but it does mean that our estimates of the role of the gene in evolution may need a correction factor, because nearly all our evidence comes from plants that are somewhat exceptional.

CHAPTER 6

Special Techniques
for the Study of Introgression

For the most part this chapter will deal with the special techniques that have been developed for apprehending introgression in the field. It should be emphasized at the outset, however, that, although these are powerful techniques and although they allow us to make reliable estimates of the probability of hybridization from field data alone, they will be more fruitful if combined with the more traditional techniques such as transplant experiments, progeny tests, cytological examination of species and hybrids, and the experimental repetition of the suspected cross. Where it is feasible to carry on this kind of experimentation it is particularly important to study *artificial backcrosses* of the hybrid to each parent. Until these have been made, one does not have even a rough estimate of how much undetected hybridization there might be in supposedly unmongrelized populations of the parental species. Of all the kinds of experimental evidence which might be gathered on such a problem, the production of artificial backcrosses is of outstanding importance. The mere demonstration that such and such a species hybrid can actually take place under natural conditions is no longer of any general significance. That these crosses can sometimes take place is now proved beyond a reasonable doubt. What we do not yet know is the role (or rather the roles) such hybridizations play in evolution. If we are going to measure the effect (or lack of effect) of hybridization in natural populations, then one of the most useful kinds of evidence we can obtain experimentally is an exact understanding of what is to be expected when the hybrid crosses back to either parent.

The chief disadvantage of these orthodox methods of hybrid analysis is that they can be applied only when the parental species are known, or at least strongly suspected. They are useful largely in proving that certain hybridizations might have taken place. They cannot be used analytically as a basis for successful prediction.

For the examination of hybrid populations or of populations in which hybridization is suspected, we need methods that record precisely the extent to which variation in one character is related to variation in other characters.

The human mind is inefficient in judging variation in more than one variable at a time. A good observer may examine three different populations and note them efficiently for their variation in pubescence, in leaf shape, or in flower color, but careful tests have shown (Anderson, unpublished) that scientists cannot look at three populations varying simultaneously in flower color *and* pubescence *and* leaf shape and render an efficient judgment of the comparative association between these characters in the three different populations.

What is needed, therefore, in describing populations is some means of recording simultaneously variation in several different characters. Species characteristically differ by slightly different proportions and trends in proportion for several different characters (Anderson and Whitaker, 1934; Anderson and Ownbey, 1939). We can differentiate most effectively between interspecific and intraspecific variation if we have some method for showing the relationships between the main variables in the population.

For such a purpose the methods of conventional biometry are laborious and inefficient. They were developed for other types of problems, and though they are fairly good for analyzing variation in any one character they are not efficient for exploring relationships between groups of characters, particularly when we do not know in advance the general nature of that relationship.

However, any methods with which we replace or precede biometrical analysis must, like it, be exact, objective, and verifiably accurate. The description and analysis of a population is one of those problems that must first be analyzed precisely on a morphological level before we can choose the best methods with which to analyze it on a mathematical level. The most effective methods so far achieved are of various sorts, but they share one feature so universally that they may be grouped under the general name of *polygraphic analysis*. That is to say that they are all more or less graphical and that they all in one way or another summarize the variation in two or more characters in a population. These various methods of *polygraphic analysis* may be listed as follows:

1. Scatter diagrams.
2. Pictorialized scatter diagrams.
3. Ideographs.
4. Hybrid indices.
5. Radiate indicators.
6. Standardized photographs.

SCATTER DIAGRAMS

Scatter diagrams are the simple alignment of dots in a two-dimensional field, such as were used in Chapter 3 in describing the possible relationships of flower color and pubescence. Since one of the steps sometimes employed in calculating the correlation coefficient is the preparation of a scatter diagram, it may be well to point out specifically that for population analysis scatter diagrams are greatly superior to the correlation coefficient as well as much easier to prepare. It is unfortunately not generally realized by most biologists that scatter diagrams may show various kinds of relationships that are ignored or distorted in the calculation of correlation coefficients (see Walker, 1943, pp. 237, 238).

PICTORIALIZED SCATTER DIAGRAMS

For all their excellencies, scatter diagrams are a somewhat limited form of polygraphic analysis because the relationships of only two characters can be considered at a time.

We can get around this handicap by letting the shape of the dot represent a third character, and the color or intensity of the dot a fourth. These pictorialized scatter diagrams are of very general usefulness in analyzing for oneself some of the main relationships in a population that one is just beginning to study. In studying variation in fields of North American maize, kernel width was diagrammed (Fig. 18) on the horizontal axis, and number of rows of kernels on the vertical axis; the shape of the dot represented the degree to which the kernel was pointed at its apex, and the intensity of the dot was proportional to the amount of soft starch in the kernels.

In making a population analysis by this method one takes a random sample of 25 ears from each corn field and records for each ear the kernel width, row number, amount of soft starch, and shape of the kernel. In the resulting diagram, each dot represents 1 ear. From the diagram as a whole, one can tell at a glance the range of variation and the average for each of these characters, as well as the relationships among all 4.

It is possible to demonstrate the reliability of the above method, though not in a quantitative way. If repeated samples of 25 are drawn from the same population, one can see at a glance that the diagrams are essentially similar. At the top of Fig. 18 are 2 samples from the same variety, with and without the addition of artificial fertilizer. At the base of the figure are 2 other varieties grown in the same Guatemalan town. It will be seen that these pictorialized scatter diagrams distinguish between varieties but give consistent results for the same variety even under somewhat different environmental conditions. This is not just a happy circumstance; 5 years of preliminary studies of many kinds of maize under various conditions of growth had been carried on before these 4 characters were finally chosen as the most reliable.

These pictorialized scatter diagrams are particularly useful because they also lend themselves to summarization. In Fig. 18 each dot represents a single ear. It is possible to cal-

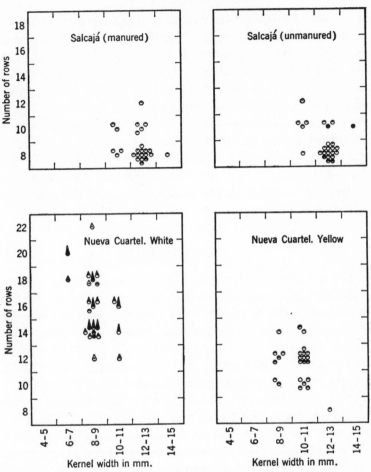

Fɪɢ. 18. Pictorialized scatter diagrams for 4 samples of maize, all from the town of Quezaltenango, Guatemala. *Above:* the same variety grown in a manured and in an unmanured plot. *Below:* two very different varieties grown in adjacent fields. In all four samples each of the 25 spots represents 1 ear of maize, the shape of the spot representing the degree to which the kernels are pointed, and the blackness indicating the relative amounts of hard and soft starch in the kernel. These four diagrams demonstrate that superficial differences due to environmental effects are scarcely apparent (note the similarity of manured and unmanured plots), while fundamental differences are made conspicuous. Though there is much variation in each, "Nueva Cuartel White" differs from "Nueva Cuartel Yellow" in having on the average more pointed kernels, more soft starch, higher row numbers, and narrower kernels.

culate an average ear from each of these samples. One can then compare the averages of fields, town by town or region by region. By this method it was possible to demonstrate (Anderson, 1946) in an exact and objective summary, how the prevailing corn type changes, within 300 miles, from the wide-kerneled, few-rowed types of western Mexico to the many-rowed, small pointed kernel types of central Mexico. By choosing appropriate characters and symbols this method can be adapted to any kind of material. On page 97, in a demonstration of the method of extrapolated correlates, pictorialized scatter diagrams are fitted to Riley's data on introgression in Iris.

IDEOGRAPHS

Though these have been employed in a number of different problems, they are not so generally useful in population studies as scatter diagrams. They are laborious to make and difficult to reproduce in quantity. However, in certain problems in which it is important to demonstrate all the relationships between a number of different measurements they are greatly superior. Ideographs are even more pictorial than scatter diagrams. In making them the original measurements are recombined in a diagram that is a more or less conventionalized representation of the object measured. They have been used extensively by Alpatov (1929) in his work on geographical differences in bees and in Anderson's studies of iris (1936c). In this latter work, the four measurements (length and width of petal; length and width of sepal) were combined to produce a figure (Fig. 19) that represented a conventionalized white petal lying on top of an equally conventionalized black sepal.

Though they are laborious to construct, the importance of ideographs lies in the fact that they show so many things at once. For the iris ideographs, each one shows fifteen separate facts. That is, if the ideographs were to be replaced with statistics, it would be necessary to employ fifteen sep-

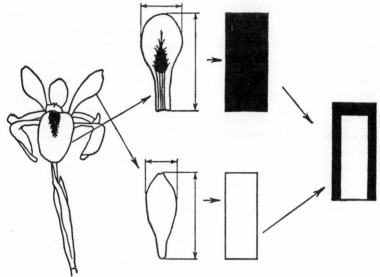

Diagram showing typical flower of *I. virginica* and resulting ideograph.

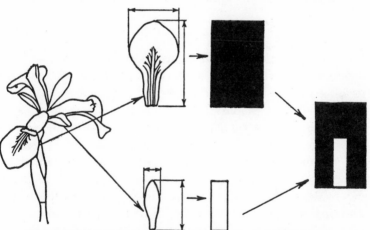

Diagram showing typical flower of *I. versicolor* and resulting ideograph.

FIG. 19. Diagrams showing how measurements for sepal length and width and for petal length and width can be grouped into "ideographs" for analyzing variation in two species of Iris.

arate measurements and ratios for each ideograph. There are first of all the four original measurements—sepal length, sepal width, petal length, and petal width; then there are the six proportions between these four, taken two at a time (the length of the petal in proportion to its width, the width of the petal in proportion to the width of the sepal, etc.); then there are four three-way relationships (such as the length-width of the petal in relation to the length of the sepal); and finally there is the relationship of all four measurements taken at once.

RADIATE INDICATORS

This type of polygraphic analysis has been used by several students of populations, notably by Norman Fassett (1941) and by Carson and Stalker (1947), but apparently has never yet been dignified with a name. Radiate indicators are useful in presenting for a number of different populations the occurrence of certain different traits or subtypes.

HYBRID INDICES

One of the most difficult types of population to analyze is one in which two or more species have hybridized freely and produced second-generation hybrids and backcrosses. Suppose, for instance, that the two species differ principally in flower color, in petal shape, and in plant height. In the second generation of hybrids and in backcrosses there will be various and multitudinous recombinations of flower colors, shapes, and heights, and no two plants will look very much alike. If we are to make an efficient comparison of two such populations, or a series of them, we must have some means of getting an overall picture of each population so that, roughly at least, we can equate one to another.

For such situations there was evolved (Anderson, 1936d) a method so crude that it was published only after its general usefulness had been demonstrated in a number of different problems. It consists in drawing up a list of differences between the hybridizing entities. All the plants in the hybrid population (or a random sample of them) are then scored individually for all these characters. Attributes like sepal length or petal length are measured; colors can be recorded by comparison with a graded series as on the Munsell and Fischer color charts. Differences in shape can be scored as essentially like one species, or like the other, or intermediate. Raunkiaer (1925) had used and published such a method for showing the great variety of character combinations to be met with in Crataegus populations. By the simple additional step of throwing all these differences together into a composite index, it was possible to extend the usefulness of this method into the domain of analysis. One could then employ it not merely to report the condition he had discovered in a certain hybrid colony but also to inquire into the forces that had produced the variation.

In the simplest application of this method each character (sepal length, petal color, height of plant, numbers of nodes, etc.) was scored in three grades: (1) similar to one species, (2) intermediate, and (3) similar to the other species. One of the species was arbitrarily selected for the low end of the scale, the other for the high end of the scale. Each character, therefore, was scored 0 if it was like the former, 2 if it was like the latter, and 1 if it was intermediate. Supposing 6 characters had been chosen for study, we would then have had a scale running from 0 to 12. Plants exactly like the first species would have scored 0 in every character, and the total score of each plant would have been 0. Plants exactly like the second would have scored 2 for each of the characters, and their total score would have been 12. Plants that were exactly intermediate would have scored 1 for each character, and their total score would have been 6. In actual practice it is usually advisable to give different score values to certain characters, either because they can be more accurately measured and therefore deserve more consideration as criteria, or because they are known to rest upon a wider genic basis and hence are representative of a large portion of the germplasm. In Riley's study of introgression in Iris (1938),*

* See Chapter 1, pp. 2–11.

tube color, sepal length, petal shape, stamen exsertion, size of style appendages, and presence of a crest were all scored as like Fulva, like HGC, or intermediate. The color of the sepal was scored in five grades from 0 to 4, and the length of the sepal in four. This gave an index running from 0 for plants like *Iris fulva* to 17 for plants like *Iris giganti-caerulea*. Riley has given a meticulous description of the way in which the hybrid index was constructed in this particular study (*loc. cit.*, pp. 727–734), to which the interested reader is referred for further details.

In such cases as hybridization between the Louisiana irises, in which the differences between the species are conspicuous and many of them are easily measured, this method is simple to apply and yields satisfactory results. When the contributing parental species are closely similar or only vaguely different, it is much less satisfactory. Hubbs and Hubbs (1943) have replaced it in their studies of hybridization in fishes with a similar but statistically more elegant method that is superior for their material. At the present time, at least for plant material, the Hybrid Index Method is a powerful means of analysis. It is efficient in exploring a complex situation and pointing out the general overall picture. In my own estimation its main application is in digging into such a problem. When the main facts have been secured, one can then work out a more precise technique adapted to any particular case. From a statistical point of view it is a crude device, and although it could easily be turned into something more respectable mathematically, for the higher plants at least, the time is premature. When we know more about hybridizing populations than we now do—when, in other words, the general problem has been more thoroughly explored on a biological level—we shall then be ready to work out more precise and elegant methods for dealing with such phenomena.

To understand the value of methods as mathematically crude as the Hybrid Index, one needs to keep in mind the general principle behind the doctrine of significant figures:

A chain of evidence is no stronger than its weakest link. Precise methods of analysis can be applied effectively only when the nature of the problem is critically understood. In dealing with anything so complicated as hybridization under natural conditions, we need a quick method for roughing out the problem. To take an actual instance, the employment of this method in the field demonstrated effectively that what at first sight appeared to be a large, more or less freely inter-breeding hybrid swarm was instead a series of highly localized populations each with its own micro-environment and its own direction of selection. Until our understanding of the dynamics of vegetation is much more precise than it is at present, we shall need simple, diagnostic field methods for summarizing in populations variation trends that are too complex for the unaided mind to grasp efficiently.

STANDARDIZED PHOTOGRAPHS

The invention of the miniature camera has made it possible to take large numbers of photographs at minimum expense. Properly standardized, such photographs become an efficient record of population variation, but they have been little used. Their earliest employment was by A. J. Wilmott of the British Museum in his studies of population differences in Salicornia. To date, their only published demonstration has been in Erickson's studies of Camassia (1941) and in the studies of maize from this laboratory (Anderson, 1947; Brown and Anderson, 1947), but they have been used extensively in various laboratories for population analysis on a variety of material.

Though it is a basically simple technique, it can be given greater precision. The first point to be borne in mind is that standardized photographs are something more than just photographs. They are exact, standardized records and need to be made in as routine a fashion as possible. Since large numbers of them will be very much alike, *it is an absolute necessity to photograph the title on each picture*, near the edge if need be, so that it can be cut out if the photograph serves as a published illustration. The background should be neutral, identical for each series, if possible, and the scale should be photographed in each picture. Two examples will show the ways in which this technique may be adapted to population problems. (1) As worked out by Dr. W. L. Brown (Brown and Anderson, 1947) for *Zea Mays:* A 10-foot white board (hinged in the middle for more ready storage) is securely fastened to the north side of a field laboratory. At 25-centimeter intervals, lines of black adhesive lantern slide tape are stretched across it to provide a scale. Down the center of the board a series of nails driven part way in and with their heads filed off provide a rack by which the corn plants can be quickly affixed to the board. Labels give the year and the record number of each plant. The leaf above the ear (usually on a sister plant) is traced on wrapping paper and photographed in a standardized position at the left of the photograph. (2) In studying Nicotiana hybrids the calyx and corolla and the dissected limb of the corolla were photographed in a standardized fashion against a frame just one half natural size. By printing these pictures on an enlarger equipped with a frame of natural size, it is a simple matter to produce a large number of exact, standardized records all of them just twice natural size.

This is one of those simple techniques that are more important than they seem. Everyone who has tried it has learned unexpected things about the material he was studying. When one sits down afterwards with a set of standardized photographs of variable populations, it is possible to see slight trends in variation or regional differences, which had completely escaped one in the field.

THE METHOD OF EXTRAPOLATED CORRELATES

The methods described above have been used in the field, in the experimental plot, and in actual plant breeding with a great variety of hybrid material. At first in a very tentative way, and later with increasing confidence, they have been employed to determine the putative parentage of hybrid swarms. The general method, which is here formally designated for the first time as the Method of Extrapolated Correlates, has a sound theoretical basis (Anderson, 1939*b;* see particularly p. 692, where the theory's application to criteria of hybridity was specifically pointed out). It was presented pragmatically by Anderson and Turrill in 1938, its application to a particular example being illustrated step by step.

The method of extrapolated correlates is based on the demonstration (set forth in detail in Chapter 3) that in a species cross all the multiple-factor characters are linked with each other (Anderson, 1939*b*). When well-differentiated entities hybridize, we may expect their cohesive forces to continue to operate for many successive generations in hybrid swarms. Certainly for scores, and perhaps for hundreds, of generations, we may expect to find the characters that went into the cross together still *tending* to stay together. By a precise and detailed examination of such populations we can discover the cohesive centers of variation still existing within them. By comparative, quantitative methods we can draw up descriptions of the original entities that must have operated to produce these centers of variation. It is possible, working with a single variable population of a species previously unknown to the investigator, to draw up a precise description of the other species which is introgressing into that population. The subsequent discovery that such a species does actually exist and could have operated in that area cannot be dismissed as a remarkable coincidence; when the prediction has been verified for a complicated series of technical details, it then becomes proof. It is even possible by this method to work with a hybrid swarm and draw up detailed descriptions of *both* parents when neither of them are known to the observer. Crude examples of such a prediction are given in Anderson and Turrill (1938) and in Anderson and Hornback (1946). The method has since been considerably refined. It will be illustrated below from the data presented in Riley's paper on introgression in Iris (Riley, 1938).

A portion of the data from Tables 1, 2, 3, and 4 of Riley's paper were presented (page 3) in Table 1 in a slightly simplified form. The figures for sepal lengths have been rounded off to the nearest centimeter. In Riley's paper the method of attack was to examine the two species first, and from a study of them attempt to analyze what was taking place in the hybrids. Using the method of extrapolated correlates, we shall demonstrate from these same data how one may work backwards *from* the introgressants, *to* the species from which they were derived. For the purposes of the illustration, therefore, let us suppose that only *Iris hexagona* var. *giganti-caerulea* is known to us and that we have come upon Colony H-2, which is much like that species on the whole yet is more variable and shows several variants outside the ordinary range of that species. In the discussion below, following the convention established in Chapter 1, we shall use HGC to designate *Iris hexagona* var. *giganti-caerulea* and Fulva to represent *Iris fulva*.

For the analysis, what we need is some simple method of determining for the whole population what characters are tending to stay together and in what patterns. We shall work with pictorialized scatter diagrams, choosing for the horizontal and vertical scales two characters each of which can be measured fairly exactly in a series of grades. In Riley's data these conditions are met by petal length and by color of sepal blade. The latter, thanks to the particular chart used by Riley, was scored in a series arranged with increasing redness from violet blue through blue violet, violet, and red violet to red. Diagramming increasing redness on the vertical axis and petal length on the horizontal axis, we produce the dots of Figs. 20 and 21 for a population of HGC and for our problem population H-2. From an inspection of these dots it is apparent that redness and petal size are tending to stick together, particularly in those individuals at the left of Fig. 21 which are outside the range of ordinary HGC. We accordingly examine Riley's table to see what other characters are varying and to see how these two extreme individuals fit into this other variation. There are five such characters, each one of which Riley scored in three grades. We add these to our large dots (each one of which

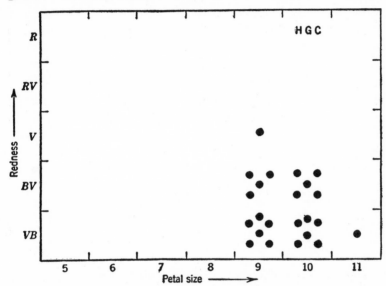

FIG. 20. Pictorialized diagram of 23 plants of *Iris hexagona* var. *giganticaerulea*, scored by the symbols shown in Fig. 23 from H. P. Riley's published data.

represents an individual plant) by using much smaller bars at five different positions around their circumferences. Tube color is represented directly above, petal shape horizontally to the right, stamen exsertion directly below, style appendages horizontally to the left, and the presence of a crest diagonally to the left. Each of these characters can be represented with no bars for one extreme grade, with a short bar for an intermediate development, and with a long bar for the other extreme.

On the hypothesis that, if redness and small petal size came into this population from the same source, other characters

may have come in with them, we assume that the peculiarities which we find tending to stay together in the two individuals at the upper left of the diagram are doing so because their genes were introduced into the population together.   Since all seven of these characters are apparently

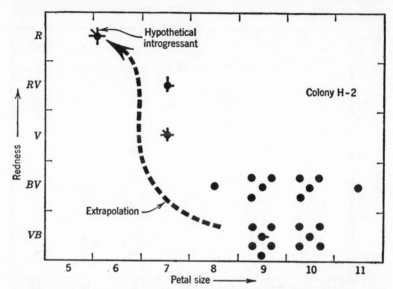

Fig. 21.   Pictorialized diagram of 23 plants from a hybrid colony studied
by Riley (see Plate 1).   Diagrammed from his data according to the
symbols of Fig. 23.   The upper-left-hand star-shaped dot represents the
hypothetical species responsible for the introgression, as determined by
the "method of extrapolated correlates."   Further discussion in the text.

multiple-factor characters, the chances are inconceivably
small that the genes for all could vary simultaneously.   That
redness, smallness, yellow tube color, petal shape, stamen
exsertion, a small style appendage, and absence of a crest
all are tending to stay together in this population is most
readily explained as due to the influx of whole chromosomes
or of chromosome segments from a species in which these
characters were tied up together.

From hybrid population H-2 there are indications that
these characters are so correlated.   By diagramming sim-

ilarly the other hybrid population H-1 (Fig. 22) in the same way we can demonstrate that these correlations hold for it and are even more strongly apparent there.

Having demonstrated the repeated existence of these complex correlations, we now proceed on the *hypothesis* that they are the result of introgression from a species in which

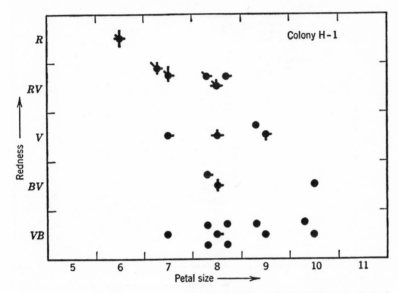

FIG. 22.   Pictorialized diagram of Hybrid Colony H-1 of Plate 1, plotted from Riley's data, using the symbols of Fig. 23.

all these characters were united. We can, therefore, extrapolate our data on the correlates in the hybrid population and produce a conception of what species would have been required to create such an effect. Population H-2 was very similar to HGC on the whole, and even H-1 bore a strong resemblance to it. Therefore, we need to imagine what kind of iris when crossed with HGC would yield such variants. If it produced reddish blue descendants in its cross with HGC, then it must have been redder still. If it produced small flowers in combination with HGC, then it must itself have had very small flowers. In this way we may extrapolate character by character from HGC to the hybrid to the other putative species. It would have had to have been an iris with very narrow, red petals, strongly exserted stamens, a yellow tube, no crest, and small stylar appendages.

Such a species having been predicted, if we can find exactly such a one in this same area, its very existence will constitute

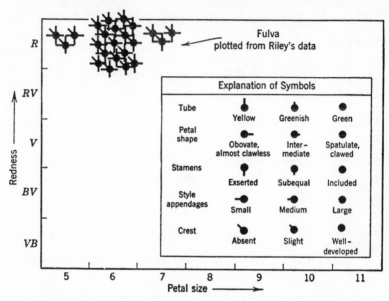

FIG. 23. Within lower-right-hand box are the symbols used in all the pictorialized scatter diagrams of Figs. 20 to 23. *Upper left:* 23 plants of *Iris fulva,* plotted from Riley's data. Note the exact correspondence with the predictions of Fig. 21.

strong evidence for the suspected hybridization. Our hypothetical introgressant, of course, proved to be Fulva. The diagram of its population plotted from Riley's data (Fig. 23) agrees exactly with our extrapolations. A series of such predictions successfully made forms almost indisputable evidence for the validity of the method of extrapolated correlates and confirms the hypothesis of introgression.

The ease of extrapolation will vary with the number of easily measured differences separating the species under observation. In a genus like Fraxinus, in which species are separated for the most part by vague and inconstant differences in texture, pubescence, etc., extrapolation will be difficult, though not impossible. The more closely related the entities involved and the more similar they are morphologically, the more difficult will it be to find differences that lend themselves to precise description and measurement. In the higher plants, however, with persistence, it has always proved possible to find suitable characters. It must be admitted that the techniques of putting such differences as leaf shape, leaf texture, and branching patterns into measurable form are still in the exploratory stage, but several that have been worked out for particular cases seem to be rather generally applicable. How far these methods can be used with other kinds of organisms it would be difficult to say. Because of the relatively simple nature of their development, plants exhibit their species differences in less complicated ways than does, for example, an insect wing or a vertebrate tooth.

In trying out such a method as that described above, one elementary fact is of great importance. If possible the work should be done in the field, at least in a preliminary way. By taking squared paper to the field it will often be possible to measure at least a few of the more obvious differences in a population and make a preliminary determination of what characters are tending to cohere in that population. As the cohering center is apprehended more and more closely, the sets of characters that go together will be more and more clearly seen. One will thus be able to collect those specimens and to concentrate on the study of those characters that are the most effective.

In interpreting and measuring the results of interspecific introgression, one of the most difficult and challenging problems is the effect of a few genes from one species when introduced into the genetic background of the other. The greater the morphological hiatus between the two hybridizing entities, the more difficult does it become to predict the impact of such a recombination or to interpret it after it has been observed. One can comparatively easily estimate the probable outcome of crossing one inbred line of maize with another and then backcrossing one or two times to the original line. It takes more experience to suggest what might be the result of such an operation upon well-differentiated species. When totally different genera (such as Zea and Tripsacum) may be concerned, the possible effect of introgression of either into the other is a research problem of no mean dimensions. One may have studied genetics for a lifetime and still be totally unable to answer the question "What would be the result of any one or two genes from Drosophila if they were introduced into *Zea Mays?*"

In introgression, what often seems at first sight to be the appearance of something totally new usually proves to be a recombination that one had not had the wit to anticipate. Hybridization ordinarily results not in the new, but in the unexpected. For example, brilliant-colored stems and leaves often appear when *Tradescantia canaliculata* suffers introgression from *Tradescantia subaspera* var. *pilosa*. Neither of these species has conspicuous plant color. Careful examination, however, shows that *T. subaspera* has a dull purple pigment in the epidermis—so dull that it gives the leaf and stem a general appearance of very dark green. *T. canaliculata* has very little color in the epidermis, but what there is has none of the dark purplish cast that characterizes *T. subaspera*. Introgression, therefore, brings some of the basic genes for colored epidermis into *T. canaliculata,* and when they operate there in the absence of the dark purple modifiers they produce a brilliant effect superficially quite different from anything in either species.

In the studies of introgression between these species it was not until after the artificial backcrosses had been made that we began to suspect the origin of the *subaspera* introgressants in *T. canaliculata*. These two species are strikingly different: *T. canaliculata* has a few long nodes, the uppermost of which are usually the longest. *T. pilosa* has many short nodes, and node length decreases progressively upwards. The introgressants of *subaspera* tend to have brilliant stems and leaves and a much higher node number than ordinary *canaliculata*. Though their nodes are somewhat shorter than in the latter, the extra number more than compensates, and the introgressants are frequently twice as tall as their unmongrelized sisters. These tallish, bright-stemmed *canaliculata*'s superficially do not look at all like *T. subaspera pilosa*. It is only when careful studies are made of leaf shape, inflorescence characters, and pubescence that one finds that the whole complex *in a greatly diluted form* is tending to stay together in these peculiar variants.

After a few examples of introgression have been studied it is much easier to recognize introgression in other genera and in other families. With active introgression, the segregation of whole chromosomes and of chromosome segments produces an overall effect on the variability of the population which, though difficult to describe, is almost unmistakable to those who have learned what it signifies. In such a population several different characters will be varying and recombining to a degree so far beyond what happens without introgression that it is of another order of magnitude. Those who have pioneered in the analysis of introgression are sometimes accused of "seeing hybrids under every bush." The truth of the matter is that, in certain groups of plants and animals, the results of hybridization are more widespread than had previously been suspected by most biologists and that the morphological effects of hybridization upon population variability are of a peculiar sort. With a little practice these peculiarities can often be recognized, even in families of plants and in floras with which the investigator is unfamiliar. By methods like those outlined above, it is possible to apply a series of critical tests to such a varying population and make valid estimates of introgression.

Epilogue

How important is introgressive hybridization? I do not know. One point seems fairly certain: its importance is paradoxical. The more imperceptible introgression becomes, the greater is its biological significance. It may be of the greatest fundamental importance when by our present crude methods we can do no more than to demonstrate its existence. When, on the other hand, it leads to bizarre hybrid swarms, apparent even to the casual passer-by, it may be of little general significance. When, as described in Woodson's studies of Asclepias populations, it produces clines reaching a third of the way across a continent, it is scarcely perceptible in any one locality. Only by the exact comparisons of populations can we demonstrate the phenomenon, yet in such populations the raw material for evolution brought in by introgression must greatly exceed the new genes produced directly by mutation. The wider spread of a few genes (if it exists) might well be imperceptible even from a study of population averages, but it would be of tremendous biological import. Germplasms are proteins, strange and complex substances. The introduction of a single alien gene into a new germplasm would be the introduction of one new unit into a gigantic protein complex. Reasoning purely from chemical facts, we might expect such a mixture to have secondary consequences in addition to its primary ones. But even were there no secondary consequences, the wide dispersal of introgressive genes (perceptible only to the most exquisitely precise techniques) would be a phenomenon of fundamental importance. Hence our paradox. Introgression is of the greater biological significance, the less is the impact apparent to casual inspection.

Bibliography

ALLAN, H. H. 1937. Wild species-hybrids in the phanerogams. *Botan. Rev., 3:*593–615.

ALPATOV, W. W. 1929. Biometrical studies on variation and races of the honey bee (*Apis mellifera* L.). *Quart. Rev. Biol., 4:*1–58.

ANDERSON, EDGAR. 1936a. A morphological comparison of triploid and tetraploid interspecific hybrids in Tradescantia. *Genetics, 21:*61–65.

——. 1936b. An experimental study of hybridization in the genus Apocynum. *Ann. Mo. Bot. Gard., 23:*159–168.

——. 1936c. The species problem in Iris. *Ann. Mo. Bot. Gard., 23:*457–509.

——. 1936d. Hybridization in American tradescantias. *Ann. Mo. Bot. Gard., 23:*511–525.

——. 1937. Cytology in its relation to taxonomy. *Botan. Rev., 3:*335–350.

——. 1939a. The hindrance to gene recombination imposed by linkage: an estimate of its total magnitude. *Am. Nat., 73:*185–188.

——. 1939b. Recombination in species crosses. *Genetics, 24:*668–698.

——. 1941. The technique and use of mass collections. *Ann. Mo. Bot. Gard., 28:*287–292.

——. 1946. Maize in Mexico: a preliminary survey. *Ann. Mo. Bot. Gard., 33:*147–247.

——. 1947. Field studies of Guatemalan maize. *Ann. Mo. Bot. Gard., 34:*433–467.

——. 1948. Hybridization of the habitat. *Evolution, 2:*1–9.

——, and RALPH O. ERICKSON. 1941. Antithetical dominance in North American maize. *Proc. Nat. Acad. Sci., 27:*436–440.

——, and EARL HORNBACK. 1946. A genetical analysis of pink daffodils: a preliminary attempt. *J. Col. Hort. Soc., 7:*334–344.

——, and LESLIE HUBRICHT. 1938. The evidence for introgressive hybridization. *Am. J. Botany, 25:*396–402.

——, and RUTH PECK OWNBEY. 1939. The genetic coefficients of specific difference. *Ann. Mo. Bot. Gard., 26:*325–348.

——, and KARL SAX. 1936. A cytological monograph of the American species of Tradescantia. *Bot. Gaz., 97:*433–476.

——, and BRENHILDA SCHAFER. 1931. Species hybrids in Aquilegia. *Ann. Bot., 45:*639–646.

103

ANDERSON, EDGAR, and BRENHILDA SCHAFER. 1933. Vicinism in *Aquilegia vulgaris*. *Am. Nat.*, *67*:1–3.

——, and W. B. TURRILL. 1938. Statistical studies on two populations of Fraxinus. *New Phytologist*, *37*:160–172.

——, and T. W. WHITAKER. 1934. Speciation in Uvularia. *J. Arnold Arboretum Harvard Univ.*, *15*:28–42.

——, and R. E. WOODSON. 1935. The species of Tradescantia indigenous to the United States. *Contribs. Arnold Arboretum*, *9*:1–132.

BALDWIN, J. T., JR. 1947. Hevea: a first interpretation. *J. Heredity*, *38*:54–64.

——, and R. E. SCHULTES. 1947. A conspectus of the genus Cunuria. *Bot. Mus. Leaflets*, *12*:325–351.

BEADLE, G. W. 1945. Biochemical genetics. *Chem. Rev.*, *37*:15–96.

BLAIR, ALBERT P. 1941*a*. Isolating mechanisms in tree frogs. *Proc. Nat. Acad. Sci.*, *27*:14–17.

——. 1941*b*. Variation, isolation mechanisms and hybridization in certain toads. *Genetics*, *26*:398–417.

BROWN, WILLIAM L., and EDGAR ANDERSON. 1947. The Northern Flint Corns. *Ann. Mo. Bot. Gard.*, *34*:1–28.

CAIN, STANLEY A. 1944. *Foundations of Plant Geography.* Harper, New York, 556 pp.

CAMP, W. H. 1942*a*. On the structure of populations in the genus Vaccinium. *Brittonia*, *4*:189–204.

——. 1942*b*. A survey of the American species of Vaccinium, subgenus Euvaccinium. *Brittonia*, *4*:205–247.

——. 1943. The herbarium in modern systematics. *Am. Nat.*, *77*:322–344.

CARSON, H. L., and H. D. STALKER. 1947. Gene arrangements in natural populations of *Drosophila robusta* Sturtevant. *Evolution*, *1*:113–133.

DANSEREAU, PIERRE. 1941. Études sur les hybrides de cistes. VI. Introgression dans la section Ladanium. *Can. J. Res.*, *19*:59–67.

DESMARAIS, YVES. 1947. Taxonomy of the sugar maples. *Am. J. Botany*, *34*:606.

EPLING, CARL C. 1947. Natural hybridization of *Salvia apiana* and *Salvia mellifera*. *Evolution*, *1*:69–78.

ERICKSON, RALPH O. 1941. Mass collections: *Camassia scilloides*. *Ann. Mo. Bot. Gard.*, *28*:287–374.

FASSETT, NORMAN C. 1941. Mass collections: *Rubus odoratus* and *R. parviflorus*. *Ann. Mo. Bot. Gard.*, *28*:299–374.

FOCKE, W. O. 1881. *Die Pflamzen-mischlinge.* Berlin, 569 pp.

FOSTER, R. C., 1937. A cyto-taxonomy survey of the North American species of Iris. *Contribs. Gray Herb.*, 99, November, 82 pp.

HEISER, CHARLES B., JR. 1947*a*. Hybridization between the sunflower species *Helianthus annuus* and *H. petiolaris*. *Evolution*, *1*:249–262.

HEISER, CHARLES B., JR. 1947*b*. Variability and hybridization in the sunflower species *Helianthus annuus* and *H. Bolanderi* in California. Ph.D. thesis (unpub.). Univ. of Calif. Library, Berkeley.

——. 1949. Hybridization in higher plants with particular reference to introgression. *Botan. Rev.*

HUBBS, CARL L., and LAURA C. HUBBS. 1943. Hybridization in nature between species of catostomid fishes. *Contribs. Lab. Vert. Biol., 22*:1–76.

HUBRICHT, LESLIE, and EDGAR ANDERSON. 1941. Vicinism in Tradescantia. *Am. J. Botany, 28*:957.

JANAKI-AMMAL, E. K. 1935. Cytogenetic studies in *Saccharum spontaneum* L. *Proc. Assoc. Ec. Biol.* (Abstract of paper.)

——. 1939. Triplo-polyploidy in *Saccharum spontaneum* L. *Curr. Sci., 8*:74–76.

——. 1941. Intergeneric hybrids of Saccharum: I–III. *J. Genetics, 41*:217–253.

——. 1942. Intergeneric hybrids of Saccharum: IV. Saccharum-Narenga. *J. Genetics, 44*:22–32.

——, and T. S. N. Singh. 1936. A preliminary note on a new Saccharum × Sorghum hybrid. *Ind. J. Agr. Sci., 6*:1105–1106.

JONES, D. F., 1920. Selection in self-fertilized lines as the basis for corn improvement. *J. Am. Soc. Agron., 12*:77–100.

LINDEGREN, CARL C., and GERTRUDE LINDEGREN. 1947. Mendelian inheritance of genes affecting vitamin-synthesizing in Saccharomyces. *Ann. Mo. Bot. Gard., 34*:95–99.

MANGELSDORF, P. C., and R. G. REEVES. 1939. The origin of Indian corn and its relatives. *Texas Ag. Exp. Sta. Bull.*, 574.

MARIE-VICTORIN, F. 1922. Esquisse systématique et écoligique de la Flore dendrologique. *Contribs. Lab. Bot. de l'Univ. de Montréal, 1*:1–33.

——. 1935. *Flore Laurentienne.* Montreal, 917 pp.

MARSDEN-JONES, E. M., and W. B. TURRILL. 1946. Researches on *Silene maritima* and *S. vulgaris. Kew Bulletin, 26*:97–107.

MASON, H. L. 1942. Evidence from the fossil record and from the modern distribution for the submergence of *Pinus remorata* by *Pinus muricata* (abs.). Committee on Geology and Geography, Rep. of the Subcommittee on Common Problems of Genetics and Paleontology (mimeographed). Nat. Res. Council.

MATHER, KENNETH. 1947. Species crosses in Antirrhinum: 1. Genetic isolation of the species *majus, glutinosum* and *orontium. Heredity, 1*:175–186.

OSBORN, A. 1941. An interesting hybrid conifer: *Cupressocyparis Leylandii. J. Roy. Hort. Soc., 66*:54–55.

OSTENFELD, C. H. 1928. The present state of knowledge on hybrids between species of flowering plants. *J. Roy. Hort. Soc., 53*:31–44.

PALMER, ERNEST J. 1948. Hybrid oaks of North America. *J. Arnold Aboretum Harvard Univ.*, *29*:1–48.

PARODI, LORENZO R. 1935. Relaciones de la agricultura prehispanica. *Am. Acad. Nac. Agron. Vit. Buenos Aires*, *1*:115–167.

RANDOLPH, L. F. 1934. Chromosome numbers in native American and introduced species and cultivated varieties of Iris. *Bull. Am. Iris Soc.*, *52*:61–66.

RAUNKIAER, C. 1925. Ermitageslettens Tjørne. *Kgl. Danske Videnskab. Biol. Meddel.*, *5*:1–76.

REED, GEORGE M. 1931. Hybrids of *Iris fulva* and *Iris foliosa*. *Brooklyn Bot. Gard. Rec.*, *20*:243–253.

RILEY, H. P. 1938. A character analysis of colonies of *Iris fulva*, *I. hexagona* var. *giganticaerulea* and natural hybrids. *Am. J. Botany*, *25*:727–738.

——. 1939*a*. Pollen fertility in Iris. *J. Heredity*, *30*:481–483.

——. 1939*b*. The problem of species in the Louisiana Irises. *Bull. Am. Iris Soc.*, 7 pp.

SAUER, CARL O. 1936. American agricultural origins: a consideration of nature and culture. *Essays in Anthropology* in honor of Alfred Louis Kroeber. Univ. of Calif. Press, Berkeley, 279 pp.

SEIBERT, R. J. 1948. The uses of Hevea for food in relation to its domestication. *Ann. Mo. Bot. Gard.*, *35*:117–121.

SMALL, J. K. 1927. Descriptions of various Iris species. *Addisonia*, *12* and *14*.

——, and E. J. ALEXANDER. 1931. Botanical interpretation of the iridaceous plants of the Gulf states. *Contribs. N. Y. Bot. Gard.*, *327*:325–357.

VALENTINE, D. H. 1948. Studies in British primulas: II. Ecology and taxonomy of primrose and oxlip *Primula vulgaris* Huds. and *P. elatior* Schreb. *New Phytologist* (in press).

VAVILOV, N. I. 1926. Studies on the origin of cultivated plants. *Bull. Appl. Bot.*, *16*:1–248.

VIOSCA, P. 1935. The irises of southeastern Louisiana. *Bull. Am. Iris Soc.*, April, 56 pp.

WALKER, HELEN M. 1943. *Elementary Statistical Methods*. Henry Holt, New York.

WIEGAND, K. M. 1935. A taxonomist's experience with hybrids in the wild. *Science*, *81*:161–166.

WOODSON, ROBERT E. 1947. Some dynamics of leaf variation in *Asclepias tuberosa*. *Ann. Mo. Bot. Gard.*, *34*:353–432.

ZIRKLE, CONWAY. 1935. *The Beginnings of Plant Hybridization*. Univ. of Penn. Press, 231 pp.

Index

Allan, 80
Alpatov, 86
Anderson, vii, 2, 12, 31, 37, 39, 43, 48, 86, 88, 91
Anderson and Hornback,vii, 93
Anderson and Hubricht, vii, 1, 12
Anderson and Ownbey, 82
Anderson and Schafer, 58
Anderson and Turrill, vii, 93
Anderson and Whitaker, 82
Antirrhinum, 58
Aquilegia, 19, 58
Asclepias, 61, 62, 64, 102

Backcross, described, 23
  importance of studying, 62, 81
Baldwin and Schultes, 78
Beadle, 13
Brown and Anderson, 91
Butterfly weed, *see Asclepias*

Cain, 63
Camp, 12, 65
Carson and Stalker, 88
Character association, as criteria for hybridity, 43
Character recombination, effect of chromosomes upon, 35
Chiasma frequency, relation to recombination, 42
Chiasma localization, relation to recombination, 42, 52
Chromosomes, cohesive effects of, 36
  effect upon character recombination, 35
Cistus, 12, 66
Cohesion, effect of linkage on, 56
  racial, 35
Crataegus, 80, 89
Cupressus × *Chamaecyparis*, 20

Dansereau, 12, 66
Desmarais, 66
Domesticated plants, origin of, 67
Drosophila, 100

Epling, 62
Erianthus, 20
Erickson, 91
Erigeron, 78
Evolution of *Helianthus* under domestication, 75
Evolution under domestication, diagram showing importance of introgression in, 69
Extrapolated correlates, method of, 93
  advantages and disadvantages, 99
  example, 94

F_1 described, 23
F_1 habitat contrasted with that of F_2, 14
F_2 habitat contrasted with that of F_1, 14
F_3, character recombination in, 49
Fagus, 65
Fassett, 88
First hybrid generation, *see* F_1
Focke, 22
Foster, 2

Gärtner, 21
Genetics, of species crosses, graphical summary, 72

Habitat, F_1 and F_2 contrasted, 14
  hybridization of, 15, 17, 18
  restriction upon hybridization, 18
Habitat preferences, inheritance of, 13

107